PRENTICE HALL MATHEMATICS

ALGEBRA 2

Chapter 9
Support File

Rational Functions

Prentice
Hall

Needham, Massachusetts
Upper Saddle River, New Jersey
Glenview, Illinois

ISBN: 0-13-063828-5

1 2 3 4 5 6 7 8 9 10   06 05 04 03 02

Prentice
Hall

Chapter 9

Rational Functions

Practice 9-1

Inverse Variation

Each ordered pair is from an inverse variation. Find the constant of variation.

1. $\left(3, \frac{1}{3}\right)$ **2.** $(0.2, 6)$ **3.** $(10, 5)$ **4.** $\left(\frac{5}{7}, \frac{2}{5}\right)$ **5.** $(3.5, 1.2)$

Suppose that x and y vary inversely. Write a function that models each inverse variation.

6. $x = 7$ when $y = 2$ **7.** $x = 4$ when $y = 9$ **8.** $x = -3$ when $y = 8$

9. $x = 5$ when $y = -6$ **10.** $x = 1$ when $y = 0.8$ **11.** $x = -4$ when $y = -2$

12. $x = \frac{3}{5}$ when $y = 5$ **13.** $x = 3$ when $y = 2.1$ **14.** $x = -\frac{1}{3}$ when $y = \frac{9}{10}$

Describe the combined variation that is modeled by each formula.

15. $I = \frac{120}{R}$ **16.** $A = \frac{1}{2}bh$ **17.** $h = \frac{3V}{B}$ **18.** $V = \frac{4}{3}\pi r^3$

Each pair of values is from an inverse variation. Find the missing value.

19. $(2, 4)$ and $(6, y)$ **20.** $\left(\frac{1}{3}, 6\right)$ and $\left(x, -\frac{1}{2}\right)$ **21.** $(1.2, 4.5)$ and $(2.7, y)$

Suppose that x and y vary inversely. Write a function that models each inverse variation, and find y when $x = 8$.

22. $x = 4$ when $y = 2$ **23.** $x = -3$ when $y = \frac{1}{3}$ **24.** $x = 6$ when $y = 1.2$

Write the function that models each relationship. Find z when $x = 6$ and $y = 4$.

25. z varies jointly with x and y. When $x = 7$ and $y = 2$, $z = 28$.

26. z varies directly with x and inversely with the cube of y. When $x = 8$ and $y = 2$, $z = 3$.

Is the relationship between the values in each table a direct variation, an inverse variation, or neither? Write equations to model the direct and inverse variations.

27.

x	2	4	5	20
y	10	5	4	1

28.

x	1	3	7	10
y	2	8	20	29

29.

x	1	2	5	7
y	6	12	30	42

30.

x	0.2	0.5	2	3
y	25	62.5	250	375

31.

x	0.1	0.5	1.5	2
y	31	7	3	2.5

32.

x	3	1.5	0.5	0.3
y	5	10	30	50

Name _____ Class _____ Date _____

Practice 9-2

Graphing Inverse Variations

Write an equation for a translation of $y = -\frac{3}{x}$ that has the given asymptotes.

1. $x = 2; y = 1$ **2.** $x = -1; y = 3$ **3.** $x = 4; y = -2$ **4.** $x = 0; y = 6$

5. $x = 3; y = 0$ **6.** $x = 1; y = 2$ **7.** $x = -3; y = -1$ **8.** $x = -2; y = 1$

Sketch the asymptotes and the graph of each equation.

9. $y = \frac{3}{x-1} + 2$ **10.** $y = \frac{2}{x+1}$ **11.** $y = \frac{11}{x+3} - 3$ **12.** $y = -\frac{4}{x-2} - 2$

13. $y = \frac{1}{x} + 3$ **14.** $y = \frac{1}{x+1} - 2$ **15.** $y = \frac{1}{x-2} + 1$ **16.** $y = \frac{1}{x-1} - 1$

17. $y = \frac{2}{x}$ **18.** $y = -\frac{3}{x-3} + 1$ **19.** $y = \frac{1}{x+1} + 2$ **20.** $y = \frac{3}{4x} + \frac{1}{2}$

21. $y = \frac{3}{x+3} - 1$ **22.** $y = \frac{2}{x-5}$ **23.** $y = -\frac{6}{x-3} - 2$ **24.** $y = \frac{5}{x}$

25. $y = \frac{1}{x-1} + 1$ **26.** $y = \frac{1}{x}$ **27.** $y = -\frac{3}{x-4} - 2$ **28.** $y = -\frac{1}{x-2} - \frac{1}{2}$

The length of a panpipe p (in feet) is inversely proportional to its pitch ℓ (in hertz). The inverse variation is modeled by the equation $p = \frac{495}{\ell}$.

29. Find the length required to produce a pitch of 220 Hz.

30. What pitch would be produced by a pipe with a length of 1.2 ft?

31. Find the pitch of a 0.6-ft pipe.

32. Find the pitch of a 3-ft pipe.

The junior class is buying keepsakes for the junior-senior prom. The price of each keepsake p is inversely proportional to the number of keepsakes s bought. The equation $p = \frac{1800}{s}$ models this inverse variation.

33. If they buy 240 keepsakes, how much can the class spend for each?

34. If they spend $5.55 for each keepsake, how many can the class buy?

35. If 400 keepsakes are bought, how much can be spent for each?

36. If the class buys 50 keepsakes, how much can be spent for each?

Compare the graphs of the inverse variations.

37. $y = \frac{1}{x}$ and $y = \frac{5}{x}$ **38.** $y = \frac{3}{x}$ and $y = -\frac{3}{x}$

39. $y = \frac{2}{x}$ and $y = \frac{20}{x}$ **40.** $y = -\frac{1}{x}$ and $y = -\frac{10}{x}$

41. $y = \frac{6}{x}$ and $y = -\frac{6}{x}$ **42.** $y = \frac{0.2}{x}$ and $y = \frac{0.02}{x}$

© Pearson Education, Inc. All rights reserved.

2   Lesson 9-2 Practice   *Algebra 2* Chapter 9

Practice 9-3

Rational Functions and Their Graphs

Find any points of discontinuity for each rational function.

1. $y = \dfrac{x + 3}{(x - 4)(x + 3)}$

2. $y = \dfrac{x - 2}{x^2 - 4}$

3. $y = \dfrac{(x - 3)(x + 1)}{(x - 2)}$

4. $y = \dfrac{3x(x + 2)}{x(x + 2)}$

5. $y = \dfrac{2}{(x + 1)}$

6. $y = \dfrac{4x}{x^3 - 9x}$

Find the horizontal asymptote of the graph of each rational function.

7. $y = \dfrac{2}{x - 6}$

8. $y = \dfrac{x + 2}{x - 4}$

9. $y = \dfrac{(x + 3)}{2(x + 4)}$

10. $y = \dfrac{2x^2 + 3}{x^2 - 6}$

11. $y = \dfrac{3x - 12}{x^2 - 2}$

12. $y = \dfrac{3x^3 - 4x + 2}{2x^3 + 3}$

Sketch the graph of each rational function.

13. $y = \dfrac{3}{x - 2}$

14. $y = \dfrac{3}{(x - 2)(x + 2)}$

15. $y = \dfrac{x}{x(x - 6)}$

16. $y = \dfrac{2x}{x - 6}$

17. $y = \dfrac{x^2 - 1}{x^2 - 4}$

18. $y = \dfrac{2x^2 + 10x + 12}{x^2 - 9}$

19. $y = \dfrac{x}{x^2 + 4}$

20. $y = \dfrac{x + 2}{x - 1}$

21. $y = \dfrac{x + 3}{x + 1}$

Describe the vertical asymptotes and holes for the graph of each rational function.

22. $y = \dfrac{x - 2}{(x + 2)(x - 2)}$

23. $y = -\dfrac{x}{x(x - 1)}$

24. $y = \dfrac{5 - x}{x^2 - 1}$

25. $y = \dfrac{x^2 - 2}{x + 2}$

26. $y = \dfrac{x^2 - 4}{x^2 + 4}$

27. $y = \dfrac{x + 3}{x^2 - 9}$

28. $y = \dfrac{x^2 - 25}{x - 4}$

29. $y = \dfrac{(x - 2)(2x + 3)}{(5x + 4)(x - 3)}$

30. $y = \dfrac{15x^2 - 7x - 2}{x^2 - 4}$

31. Suppose you start a home business typing technical research papers for college students. You must spend $3500 to replace your computer system. Then you estimate the cost of typing each page will be $.02.

   a. Write a rational function modeling your average cost per page. Graph the function.

   b. How many pages must you type to bring your average cost per page to less than $1.50 per page, the amount you plan to charge?

   c. How many pages must you type to have the average cost per page equal $1.00?

   d. How many pages must you type to have the average cost per page equal $.50?

   e. What are the vertical and horizontal asymptotes of the graph of the function?

Practice 9-4

Rational Expressions

Simplify each rational expression. State any restrictions on the variable.

1. $\dfrac{20 + 40x}{20x}$

2. $\dfrac{4x + 6}{2x + 3}$

3. $\dfrac{3y^2 - 3}{y^2 - 1}$

4. $\dfrac{4x + 20}{3x + 15}$

5. $\dfrac{x^2 + x}{x^2 + 2x}$

6. $\dfrac{3x + 6}{5x + 10}$

7. $\dfrac{2y}{y^2 + 6y}$

8. $\dfrac{x^2 - 5x}{x^2 - 25}$

9. $\dfrac{x^2 + 3x - 18}{x^2 - 36}$

10. $\dfrac{x^2 + 13x + 40}{x^2 - 2x - 35}$

11. $\dfrac{3x^2 - 12}{x^2 - x - 6}$

12. $\dfrac{4x^2 - 36}{x^2 + 10x + 21}$

13. $\dfrac{2x^2 + 11x + 5}{3x^2 + 17x + 10}$

14. $\dfrac{6x^2 + 5x - 6}{3x^2 - 5x + 2}$

15. $\dfrac{7x - 28}{x^2 - 16}$

16. $\dfrac{x^2 - 9}{2x + 6}$

Multiply or divide. Write the answer in simplest form. State any restrictions on the variables.

17. $\dfrac{5a}{5a + 5} \cdot \dfrac{10a + 10}{a}$

18. $\dfrac{9 - x^2}{5x^3 + 17x^2 + 6x} \cdot \dfrac{5x^2 + 2x}{x - 3}$

19. $\dfrac{(x - 1)(2x - 4)}{x + 4} \cdot \dfrac{(x + 1)(x + 4)}{2x - 4}$

20. $\dfrac{(x + 3)(x + 4)}{(x + 1)(x + 3)} \cdot \dfrac{(x + 3)(x + 1)}{x + 4}$

21. $\dfrac{5y - 20}{3y + 15} \cdot \dfrac{7y + 35}{10y + 40}$

22. $\dfrac{3x^3}{x^2 - 25} \cdot \dfrac{x^2 + 6x + 5}{x^2}$

23. $\dfrac{3y + 3}{6y + 12} \div \dfrac{18}{5y + 5}$

24. $\dfrac{6x + 6}{7} \div \dfrac{4x + 4}{x - 2}$

25. $\dfrac{y^2 - 2y}{y^2 + 7y - 18} \cdot \dfrac{y^2 - 81}{y^2 - 11y + 18}$

26. $\dfrac{(y + 6)^2}{y^2 - 36} \cdot \dfrac{3y - 18}{2y + 12}$

27. $\dfrac{y^2 - 49}{(y - 7)^2} \div \dfrac{5y + 35}{y^2 - 7y}$

28. $\dfrac{x^2 - 3x - 10}{2x^2 - 11x + 5} \div \dfrac{x^2 - 5x + 6}{2x^2 - 7x + 3}$

29. $\dfrac{x^2 - 5x + 4}{x^2 - 1} \cdot \dfrac{x^2 + 5x + 4}{x^2 - 9}$

30. $\dfrac{x^2 - 5x}{x^2 + 3x} \cdot \dfrac{x + 3}{x - 5}$

31. $\dfrac{x^2 - 4}{x^2 + 6x + 9} \cdot \dfrac{x^2 - 9}{x^2 + 4x + 4}$

32. $\dfrac{x^2 - 6x}{x^2 - 36} \cdot \dfrac{x + 6}{x^2}$

33. $\dfrac{x^2 + 10x + 16}{x^2 - 6x - 16} \div \dfrac{x + 8}{x^2 - 64}$

34. $\dfrac{5y}{2x^2} \div \dfrac{5y^2}{8x^2}$

35. $\dfrac{6x^2 - 32x + 10}{3x^2 - 15x} \div \dfrac{3x^2 + 11x - 4}{2x^2 - 32}$

36. $\dfrac{7x^4}{24y^5} \div \dfrac{21x}{12y^4}$

37. $\dfrac{2x + 4}{10x} \cdot \dfrac{15x^2}{x + 2}$

38. $\dfrac{x^2 + 6x}{3x^2 + 6x - 24} \cdot \dfrac{x^2 + 2x - 8}{x + 6}$

39. $\dfrac{x^2 - 5x + 4}{x^2 + 3x - 28} \cdot \dfrac{x^2 + 2x - 3}{x^2 + 10x + 21}$

40. $\dfrac{x^2 + 2x + 1}{x^2 - 1} \cdot \dfrac{x^2 + 3x + 2}{x^2 + 4x + 4}$

Practice 9-5

Find the least common multiple of each pair of polynomials.

1. $3x(x + 2)$ and $6x(2x - 3)$

2. $2x^2 - 8x + 8$ and $3x^2 + 27x - 30$

3. $4x^2 + 12x + 9$ and $4x^2 - 9$

4. $2x^2 - 18$ and $5x^3 + 30x^2 + 45x$

Simplify.

5. $\dfrac{x^2}{5} + \dfrac{x^2}{5}$

6. $\dfrac{x^2 - 2}{12} + \dfrac{x}{6}$

7. $\dfrac{12}{xy^3} - \dfrac{9}{xy^3}$

8. $-\dfrac{2}{n + 4} - \dfrac{n^2}{n^2 - 16}$

9. $\dfrac{x}{9} - \dfrac{2x}{9}$

10. $\dfrac{2y + 1}{3y} + \dfrac{5y + 4}{3y}$

11. $\dfrac{6y - 4}{y^2 - 5} + \dfrac{3y + 1}{y^2 - 5}$

12. $\dfrac{6}{5x^2y} + \dfrac{5}{10xy^2}$

13. $\dfrac{3}{8x^3y^3} - \dfrac{1}{4xy}$

14. $\dfrac{4}{x^2 - 25} + \dfrac{6}{x^2 + 6x + 5}$

15. $\dfrac{3}{7x^2y} + \dfrac{4}{21xy^2}$

16. $\dfrac{xy - y}{x - 2} - \dfrac{y}{x + 2}$

17. $\dfrac{x + 2}{x^2 + 4x + 4} + \dfrac{2}{x + 2}$

18. $\dfrac{3}{x^2 - x - 6} + \dfrac{2}{x^2 + 6x + 5}$

19. $\dfrac{1}{6x^2 - 11x + 3} + \dfrac{1}{8x^2 - 18}$

20. $\dfrac{4}{x^2 - 3x} + \dfrac{6}{3x - 9}$

21. $\dfrac{3}{x^2 + 3x - 10} + \dfrac{1}{x^2 + 6x + 5}$

22. $\dfrac{3}{x - 9} + 4x$

23. $3 - \dfrac{1}{x^2 + 5}$

24. $5 + \dfrac{1}{x^2 - 5x + 6}$

25. $1 + \dfrac{2x + 7}{3x - 1}$

26. $\dfrac{2a}{a + 2} + \dfrac{3a}{a - 2}$

27. $\dfrac{4c}{c - 3} + \dfrac{4c}{c + 3}$

28. $\dfrac{f + 1}{fgh} + \dfrac{f - 1}{fgh}$

29. $\dfrac{2 - t}{t - 5} + \dfrac{2 + t}{t + 5}$

30. $\dfrac{4r}{r - 2} + \dfrac{4r}{r + 2}$

31. $\dfrac{x - y}{x + y} + \dfrac{y}{x}$

32. $\dfrac{\frac{2}{x}}{\frac{3}{y}}$

33. $\dfrac{1 + \frac{2}{x}}{4 - \frac{6}{x}}$

34. $\dfrac{\frac{1}{x - 2}}{2 + \frac{1}{x}}$

35. $\dfrac{y}{4y + 8} - \dfrac{1}{y^2 + 2y}$

36. $\dfrac{1 + \frac{2}{3}}{\frac{4}{9}}$

37. $\dfrac{6x^2}{3x - 2} + \dfrac{5x - 6}{3x - 2}$

38. $\dfrac{\frac{3}{x + 1}}{\frac{5}{x - 1}}$

39. $\dfrac{\frac{2}{x} + 6}{\frac{1}{y}}$

40. $\dfrac{2y}{y^2 - 4y - 12} + \dfrac{y}{y^2 - 10y + 24}$

41. The total resistance for a parallel circuit is given by

$\dfrac{1}{R} = \dfrac{1}{R_1} + \dfrac{1}{R_2} + \dfrac{1}{R_3}$.

   a. If $R = 1$ ohm, $R_2 = 6$ ohms, and $R_3 = 8$ ohms, find R_1.

   b. If $R_1 = 3$ ohms, $R_2 = 4$ ohms, and $R_3 = 6$ ohms, find R.

Practice 9-6

Solve each equation. Check each solution.

1. $\frac{1}{x} = \frac{x}{9}$

2. $\frac{4}{x} = \frac{x}{4}$

3. $\frac{3x}{4} = \frac{5x + 1}{3}$

4. $-\frac{4}{x + 1} = \frac{5}{3x + 1}$

5. $\frac{3}{2x - 3} = \frac{1}{5 - 2x}$

6. $\frac{x - 4}{3} = \frac{x - 2}{2}$

7. $\frac{3}{1 - x} = \frac{2}{1 + x}$

8. $\frac{2x - 3}{4} = \frac{2x - 5}{6}$

9. $\frac{1}{x} = \frac{2}{x + 3}$

10. $\frac{x - 1}{6} = \frac{x}{4}$

11. $\frac{3 - x}{6} = \frac{6 - x}{12}$

12. $\frac{4}{x + 3} = \frac{10}{2x - 1}$

13. $\frac{x - 2}{10} = \frac{x - 7}{5}$

14. $\frac{3}{3 - x} = \frac{4}{2 - x}$

15. $\frac{1}{4 - 5x} = \frac{3}{x + 9}$

16. $x + \frac{10}{x - 2} = \frac{x^2 + 3x}{x - 2}$

17. $\frac{2}{x + 3} + \frac{5}{3 - x} = \frac{6}{x^2 - 9}$

18. $\frac{1}{2x + 2} + \frac{5}{x^2 - 1} = \frac{1}{x - 1}$

19. $\frac{2}{6x + 2} = \frac{x}{3x^2 + 11}$

20. $\frac{3}{2x - 4} = \frac{5}{3x + 7}$

21. $\frac{2y}{5} + \frac{2}{6} = \frac{y}{2} - \frac{1}{6}$

22. $\frac{1}{2x + 2} = \frac{1}{x - 1}$

23. $\frac{2}{x + 2} + \frac{5}{x - 2} = \frac{6}{x^2 - 4}$

24. $5 + \frac{5}{x} = \frac{6}{5x}$

25. $\frac{4}{x - 1} = \frac{5}{x - 2}$

26. $\frac{2x - 1}{x + 3} = \frac{5}{3}$

27. $\frac{7}{2} = \frac{7x}{8} - 4$

28. $5 - \frac{4}{x + 1} = 6$

29. $\frac{x}{x + 3} - \frac{x}{x - 3} = \frac{x^2 + 9}{x^2 - 9}$

30. $\frac{x}{3} + \frac{x}{2} = 10$

31. $\frac{2}{3} + \frac{3x - 1}{6} = \frac{5}{2}$

32. $4 + \frac{2y}{y - 5} = \frac{8}{y - 5}$

33. $\frac{4}{x - 3} = \frac{2}{x + 1} + \frac{16}{x^2 - 2x - 3}$

34. $\frac{7}{x^2 - 5x} + \frac{2}{x} = \frac{3}{2x - 10}$

35. $\frac{x + 3}{x^2 + 3x - 4} = \frac{x + 2}{x^2 - 16}$

36. $\frac{3y}{5} + \frac{1}{2} = \frac{y}{10}$

37. A round trip flight took 3.9 h flying time. The plane traveled the 510 mi to the city at 255 mi/h with no wind. How strong was the wind on the return flight? Was the wind a head wind or a tail wind?

38. A round trip flight took 5 h flying time. The plane traveled the 720 mi to the city at 295 mi/h with no wind. How strong was the wind on the return flight? Was the wind a head wind or a tail wind?

39. If one student can complete the decorations for the prom in 5 days working alone, another student could do it in 3 days, and a third could do it in 4 days, how long would it take them working together?

40. Tom and Huck start a business painting fences. They paint Aunt Polly's fence and find that they can paint a 200-ft² fence in 40 min if they work together. If Huck works four times faster than Tom, how long would it take each of them to paint a 500-ft² fence working alone?

Practice 9-7

Integers from 1 to 100 are randomly selected. State whether the events are mutually exclusive.

1. Even integers and multiples of 3

2. Integers less than 40 and integers greater than 50

3. Odd integers and multiples of 4

4. Integers less than 50 and integers greater than 40

Classify each pair of events as *dependent* or *independent*.

5. A member of the junior class and a second member of the same class are randomly selected.

6. A member of the junior class and a member of another class are randomly chosen.

7. An odd-numbered problem is assigned for homework, and an even-numbered problem is picked for a test.

8. The sum and the product of two rolls of a number cube

Find each probability.

9. A flavored-water company wants to know how many people prefer its new lemon-flavored water over two competitors' brands. The company hires you to survey 1000 people and ask them to rank the three drinks in order of preference. After conducting the survey, you find that 35% prefer the lemon-flavored water over Competitor A, 38% prefer the lemon-flavored water over Competitor B, and 47% did not prefer the lemon-flavored water over either competitor's brand. What is the probability that someone prefers the lemon-flavored water over both competitors' brands?

10. A natural number from 1 to 10 is randomly chosen.
  a. P(even or 7)
  b. P(even or odd)
  c. P(multiple of 2 or multiple of 3)
  d. P(odd or less than 3)

11. A standard number cube is tossed.
  a. P(even or 3)
  b. P(less than 2 or even)
  c. P(prime or 4)
  d. P(2 or greater than 6)

12. Only 93% of the airplane parts Salome is examining pass inspection. What is the probability that all of the next five parts pass inspection?

13. There is a 50% chance of thunderstorms the next three days. What is the probability that there will be thunderstorms each of the next three days?

***Q* and *R* are independent events. Find *P*(*Q* and *R*).**

14. $P(Q) = \frac{1}{8}, P(R) = \frac{2}{5}$

15. $P(Q) = 0.8, P(R) = 0.2$

16. $P(Q) = \frac{1}{4}, P(R) = \frac{1}{5}$

***M* and *N* are mutually exclusive events. Find *P*(*M* or *N*).**

17. $P(M) = \frac{3}{4}, P(N) = \frac{1}{6}$

18. $P(M) = 10\%, P(N) = 45\%$

19. $P(M) = \frac{1}{5}, P(N) = 18\%$

Reteaching 9-1

Inverse Variation

| **OBJECTIVE:** Identifying and solving inverse variations | **MATERIALS:** None |

- In a direct variation, $y = kx$, as the value of one variable increases, so does the other. For inverse variation, $y = \frac{k}{x}$, as the value of one variable increases, the value of the other decreases.

Example

The time t that is necessary to complete a task varies inversely as the number of people p working. If it takes 4 h for 12 people to paint the exterior of a house, how long would it take for 3 people to do the same job?

$t = \frac{k}{p}$ ← **Write an inverse variation. Since time is dependent on people, t is the dependent variable and p is the independent variable.**

$4 = \frac{k}{12}$ ← **Substitute 4 for t and 12 for p.**

$48 = k$ ← **Multiply both sides by 12 to solve for k, the constant of variation.**

$t = \frac{48}{p}$ ← **Substitute 48 for k. This is the equation of the inverse variation.**

$t = \frac{48}{3} = 16$ ← **Substitute 3 for p. Simplify to solve the equation.**

It would take 3 people 16 h to paint the exterior of the house.

Exercises

1. The time t needed to complete a task varies inversely as the number of people p. It takes 5 h for seven men to install a new roof. How long would it take ten men to complete the job?

2. The time t needed to drive a certain distance varies inversely as the speed r. It takes 7.5 h at 40 mi/h to drive a certain distance. How long would it take to drive the same distance at 60 mi/h?

3. The cost of each item bought is inversely proportional to the number of items when spending a fixed amount. When 42 items are bought, each costs $1.46. Find the number of items when each costs $2.16 each.

4. The length ℓ of a rectangle of a certain area varies inversely as the width w. The length of a rectangle is 9 cm when its width is 6 cm. Determine its length if its width is 8 cm.

Reteaching 9-2

Graphing Inverse Variations

OBJECTIVE: Identifying asymptotes and graphing inverse variations	**MATERIALS:** None

- An inverse variation equation has the form $y = \frac{k}{x}$. Its graph has vertical and horizontal asymptotes on the x- and y-axes.

- When an equation is of the form $y = \frac{k}{x-b} + c$, it is a translation of the inverse variation graph $y = \frac{k}{x}$. This means that the graph is moved b units to the left or right and c units up or down. The asymptotes are found at $x = b$ and $y = c$.

Example

Sketch the graph of $y = -\frac{6}{x-3} + 2$, and include any asymptotes.

$y = -\frac{6}{x-3} + 2$ ← **Check to see that the equation is in $y = \frac{k}{x-b} + c$ form.**

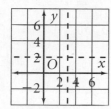

← **Because $b = 3$ and $c = 2$, the vertical asymptote will occur at $x = 3$ and the horizontal asymptote at $y = 2$.**

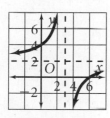

← **Because k is negative, the branches occur in the upper–left and lower–right regions. When k is positive, the branches occur in the upper–right and lower–left regions.**

Exercises

Sketch the asymptotes and the graph of each function.

1. $y = \frac{8}{x}$

2. $y = -\frac{4}{x}$

3. $xy = 2$

4. $y = \frac{2}{x+4}$

5. $y = -\frac{4}{x-8}$

6. $y = -\frac{2}{x} + 3$

7. $y = \frac{1}{x} - 4$

8. $y = -\frac{2}{x+3} - 3$

9. $y = \frac{2}{x-3} + 4$

10. $y = \frac{3}{x-2} - 4$

11. $y = \frac{2}{3x} + \frac{3}{2}$

12. $y = -\frac{2}{x+2} + 3$

Reteaching 9-3

Rational Functions and Their Graphs

OBJECTIVE: Finding and classifying points of discontinuity

MATERIALS: None

Rational functions may have two different types of points of discontinuity.

- A hole is present at $x = a$ when a is a zero of both the numerator and the denominator.

- A vertical asymptote is present at $x = a$ when a is a zero of the denominator only.

- Find points of discontinuity before attempting to graph the function.

Example

Find and classify any points of discontinuity for $y = \dfrac{x^2 + x - 6}{3x^2 - 12}$.

$y = \dfrac{x^2 + x - 6}{3x^2 - 12}$

$y = \dfrac{(x - 2)(x + 3)}{3(x - 2)(x + 2)}$ ⟵ **Factor the numerator and denominator completely.**

$y = \dfrac{(x - 2)(x + 3)}{3(x - 2)(x + 2)}$ ⟵ **Circle common factors in the numerator and denominator to indicate holes.**

$x - 2 = 0$ ⟵ **Use the Zero-Product Property to find the point of discontinuity.**

$x = 2$

$x + 2 = 0$
$x = -2$ ⟵ **Use the Zero-Product Property with any remaining factors in the denominator to find the asymptotes.**

There is a hole at $x = 2$ and a vertical asymptote at $x = -2$.

Exercises

Find and classify any points of discontinuity.

1. $y = \dfrac{x}{x^2 - 9}$

2. $y = \dfrac{3x^2 - 1}{x^3}$

3. $y = \dfrac{6x^2 + 3}{x - 1}$

4. $y = \dfrac{5x^3 - 4}{x^2 + 4x - 5}$

5. $y = \dfrac{7x}{x^3 + 1}$

6. $y = \dfrac{12x^4 + 10x - 3}{3x^4}$

7. $y = \dfrac{12x + 24}{x^2 + 2x}$

8. $y = \dfrac{x^2 - 1}{x^2 + 3x + 2}$

9. $y = \dfrac{x^2 - 1}{x^2 - 2x - 3}$

Reteaching 9-4

OBJECTIVE: Multiplying and dividing rational expressions	**MATERIALS:** None

Example

Divide $\dfrac{x^2-2x-35}{2x^3-3x^2}$ by $\dfrac{7x-49}{4x^3-9x}$.

$$\dfrac{x^2 - 2x - 35}{2x^3 - 3x^2} \div \dfrac{7x - 49}{4x^3 - 9x}$$

$$= \dfrac{x^2 - 2x - 35}{2x^3 - 3x^2} \cdot \dfrac{4x^3 - 9x}{7x - 49} \qquad \longleftarrow \quad \textbf{Multiply by the reciprocal of the second expression.}$$

$$= \dfrac{(x - 7)(x + 5)}{x \cdot x(2x - 3)} \cdot \dfrac{x(2x - 3)(2x + 3)}{7(x - 7)} \qquad \longleftarrow \quad \textbf{Factor expressions completely.}$$

$$= \dfrac{\cancel{(x - 7)}(x + 5)}{\cancel{x} \cdot x\cancel{(2x - 3)}} \cdot \dfrac{\cancel{x}\cancel{(2x - 3)}(2x + 3)}{7\cancel{(x - 7)}} \qquad \longleftarrow \quad \textbf{Divide out common factors.}$$

$$= \dfrac{2x^2 + 13x + 15}{7x} \qquad \longleftarrow \quad \textbf{Multiply remaining factors.}$$

Exercises

Multiply or divide. Write the result in simplest form.

1. $\dfrac{x^2 - y^2}{(x - y)^2} \cdot \dfrac{1}{x + y}$

2. $\dfrac{a^2 - a - 6}{a^2 - 7a + 12} \cdot \dfrac{a^2 - 2a - 8}{a^2 - 3a - 10}$

3. $\dfrac{3x + 12}{2x - 8} \div \dfrac{x^2 + 8x + 16}{x^2 - 8x + 16}$

4. $\dfrac{2x}{3x - 12} \div \dfrac{x^2 - 2x}{x^2 - 6x + 8}$

5. $\dfrac{4x^2 - 4x}{x^2 + 2x - 3} \cdot \dfrac{x^2 + x - 6}{4x}$

6. $\dfrac{x^2 + 3x}{x^2 + 6x + 8} \cdot \dfrac{-(x^2 + x - 2)}{4x^3 + 12x^2}$

7. $\dfrac{2x^2 - 16x}{x^2 - 9x + 8} \div \dfrac{2x}{5x - 5}$

8. $\dfrac{x - 3}{x^2 - 5x - 14} \div \dfrac{x^2 - x - 6}{x - 7}$

9. $\dfrac{2x - 10}{3x - 21} \div \dfrac{x - 5}{4x - 28}$

10. $\dfrac{x^2 - 9x + 14}{x^3 + 2x^2} \div \dfrac{x - 2}{x + 2}$

11. $\dfrac{x^2 + 2x - 8}{x^2} \cdot \dfrac{x^2 - 3x}{x^2 + x - 12}$

12. $\dfrac{x^2 + 3x}{x^2 - 3x + 2} \cdot \dfrac{x^2 + x - 2}{3x^2 + 9x}$

13. $\dfrac{4x - 16}{4x} \div \dfrac{x^2 - 2x - 8}{3x + 6}$

14. $\dfrac{3x - 12}{2x^2 - 8x} \div \dfrac{x^2 + x - 6}{x^3 - 4x}$

15. $\dfrac{x^4 - 9x^2}{x^3 + 3x^2} \cdot \dfrac{3x}{x^2 - 3x}$

16. $\dfrac{1}{x^4 - x^3 - 2x^2} \cdot \dfrac{x^2 - x - 2}{x^2}$

Reteaching 9-5

Adding and Subtracting Rational Expressions

OBJECTIVE: Adding and subtracting rational expressions

MATERIALS: None

- To find the sum or difference of two rational expressions with like denominators, simply add or subtract their numerators. Then write the answer over the common denominator.

- To find the sum or difference of two rational expressions with unlike denominators, first find the least common denominator. Then multiply each fraction by the factors needed to get the least common denominator. Remember, the factor(s) multiplied should always be in fraction form and equivalent to 1—for example, $\frac{x+1}{x+1}$.

Example

Subtract: $\frac{2x}{3x+5} - \frac{14}{x+7}$. Simplify, if possible.

$$\frac{2x}{3x+5} - \frac{14}{x+7}$$

$$\frac{2x}{\boxed{3x+5}} - \frac{14}{\boxed{x+7}} \qquad \longleftarrow \quad \textbf{Circle the factors multiplied to get the least common denominator.}$$

$$= \frac{2x(x+7)}{(3x+5)(x+7)} - \frac{14(3x+5)}{(3x+5)(x+7)} \qquad \longleftarrow \quad \textbf{Multiply as necessary to rewrite with the least common denominator.}$$

$$= \frac{(2x^2+14x)}{(3x+5)(x+7)} - \frac{(42x+70)}{(3x+5)(x+7)} \qquad \longleftarrow \quad \textbf{Use the Distributive Property in the numerator.}$$

$$= \frac{2x^2+14x-42x-70}{(3x+5)(x+7)} \qquad \longleftarrow \quad \textbf{Subtract the numerators of the fractions.}$$

$$= \frac{2x^2-28x-70}{(3x+5)(x+7)} \qquad \longleftarrow \quad \textbf{Combine like terms.}$$

The difference is $\frac{2x^2-28x-70}{(3x+5)(x+7)}$.

Exercises

Add or subtract. Simplify, if possible.

1. $\frac{3}{2a+3} + \frac{2a}{2a+3}$

2. $\frac{y}{y-1} + \frac{2}{1-y}$

3. $\frac{3}{x+2} + \frac{2}{x^2-4}$

4. $\frac{y}{y^2-y-20} + \frac{2}{y+4}$

5. $\frac{x}{x^2+5x+6} - \frac{2}{x^2+3x+2}$

6. $\frac{4x+1}{x^2-4} - \frac{3}{x-2}$

7. $-\frac{2}{7x} - \frac{5}{4x}$

8. $\frac{12x^2-x+9}{3x+33} - \frac{16}{x+11}$

9. $\frac{4}{x^2+3x} + \frac{5}{x^3-2x^2}$

Reteaching 9-6

Solving Rational Equations

OBJECTIVE: Solving rational equations	**MATERIALS:** None

- When one side of a rational equation has a sum or difference, multiply each side by the LCD. This eliminates the fractions.

Example

Solve the equation.

$$\frac{6}{x} + \frac{x}{2} = 4$$

$$2x\left(\frac{6}{x}\right) + 2x\left(\frac{x}{2}\right) = 2x(4) \qquad \longleftarrow \text{ Multiply the LCD, } 2x, \text{ by each term.}$$

$$2x\left(\frac{6}{x}\right) + 2x\left(\frac{x}{2}\right) = 2x(4) \qquad \longleftarrow \text{ Cancel where possible.}$$

$$12 + x^2 = 8x \qquad \longleftarrow \text{ Simplify.}$$

$$x^2 - 8x + 12 = 0 \qquad \longleftarrow \text{ Write the equation in standard form.}$$

$$(x - 2)(x - 6) = 0 \qquad \longleftarrow \text{ Factor.}$$

$$x - 2 = 0 \quad x - 6 = 0 \qquad \longleftarrow \text{ Use the Zero-Product Property to solve for } x.$$

$$x = 2 \qquad x = 6$$

Exercises

Solve each equation. Check each solution.

1. $\dfrac{10}{x + 3} + \dfrac{10}{3} = 6$

2. $-\dfrac{1}{x - 3} = \dfrac{x - 4}{x^2 - 27}$

3. $\dfrac{6}{x - 1} + \dfrac{2x}{x - 2} = 2$

4. $\dfrac{7}{3x - 12} - \dfrac{1}{x - 4} - \dfrac{2}{3}$

5. $\dfrac{2x}{5} = \dfrac{x^2 - 5x}{5x}$

6. $\dfrac{8(x - 1)}{x^2 - 4} - \dfrac{4}{x - 2}$

7. $x + \dfrac{4}{x} = \dfrac{25}{6}$

8. $\dfrac{2}{x} + \dfrac{6}{x - 1} = \dfrac{6}{x^2 - x}$

9. $\dfrac{2}{x} + \dfrac{1}{x} = 3$

10. $\dfrac{4}{x - 1} = \dfrac{5}{x - 1} + 2$

11. $\dfrac{1}{x} = \dfrac{5}{2x} + 3$

12. $\dfrac{x + 6}{5} = \dfrac{2x - 4}{5} - 3$

13. Quinn can refinish hardwood floors four times as fast as Jack. They have to refinish 100 ft^2 of flooring. Working together, Quinn and Jack can finish the job in 3 hours. How long would it take each of them working alone?

Reteaching 9-7

Probability of Multiple Events

| **OBJECTIVE:** Finding probabilities of multiple events | **MATERIALS:** Colored pencils |

Example

Find the probability. A cage at the pet store contains ten white mice. Out of the ten, there are four females and six males. There are also ten black mice, of which six are female and four are male. Suppose you reach into the cage and randomly pick one mouse. What is the probability that the one you selected is female or black?

Step 1: Make a table of possibilities. These are events that can happen at the same time. The events are not mutually exclusive.

Step 2: Find P(female) by putting a circle around each female mouse.

$$P\text{(female)} = \frac{10}{20} = \frac{1}{2}$$

Step 3: Find P(black) by putting an "X" through each black mouse.

$$P\text{(black)} = \frac{10}{20} = \frac{1}{2}$$

Step 4: Find the events that have both a circle and an "X."

$$P\text{(female and black)} = \frac{6}{20} = \frac{3}{10}$$

Step 5: Use the formula $P(A \text{ or } B) = P(A) + P(B) - P(A \text{ and } B)$ to find P(female or black).

$$\frac{10}{20} + \frac{10}{20} - \frac{6}{20} = \frac{14}{20} = \frac{7}{10}, \text{ or } 70\%$$

The probability that you select a mouse that is female or black is 70%.

Ⓕ w	Ⓕ w	Ⓕ w	Ⓕ w
m w	m w	m w	m w
m w	m w	Ⓕ X̶	Ⓕ X̶
Ⓕ X̶	Ⓕ X̶	Ⓕ X̶	Ⓕ X̶
m X̶	m X̶	m X̶	m X̶

Exercises

Find the probability of each event.

1. Use the information from the example above to find the probability of selecting a mouse that is either white or male. Use the same table, but use a pencil of a different color.

2. A bag of marbles contains 13 marbles that are opaque and 32 marbles that are translucent. Of the opaque marbles, 3 are red, 5 are blue, and 5 are green. Of the translucent marbles, 8 are red, 12 are blue and 12 are green. What is the probability that you randomly pick a marble that is red or opaque?

3. Use the table you constructed for Exercise 2 and a different color marker to find the probability that you randomly pick a marble that is green or translucent.

Enrichment 9-1
....
Ahead of His Time

One famous geologist was actually a professor of meteorology. He became interested in why the western coast of Africa seemed to fit together with the eastern coast of South America. In 1910, he announced his theory of continental drift.

To find out the name of this famous geologist, solve the following problems for z. Then use the value of z to place the letter found in brackets at the end of the problem in the corresponding space in the diagram below.

$\overline{}\ \overline{}\ \overline{}\ \overline{}\ \overline{}\ \overline{}\ \overline{}\ \overline{}\ \overline{}\ \overline{}\ \overline{}\ \overline{}\ \overline{}\ \overline{}$
　1　　2　　3　　4　　5　　6　　7　　8　　9　　10　　11　　12　　13　　14

1. z varies directly as the square of y and inversely as x. If $x = 2$ and $y = 4$, then $z = 16$. Find z if $x = 2$ and $y = 1$. [A]

2. z varies directly as the cube of x and inversely as the square of y. If $x = 1$ and $y = 2$, then $z = 3$. Find z if $x = 2$ and $y = 4$. [D]

3. z varies directly as x and inversely as y. If $x = 2$ and $y = 4$, then $z = 13$. Find z if $x = 5$ and $y = 10$. [E]

4. z varies directly as the square of x and inversely as y. If x and y are both equal to 3, then $z = 30$. Find z if $x = 1$ and $y = 2$. [E]

5. z varies directly as the fourth power of x and inversely as the cube of y. If both x and y are equal to 1, $z = 3$. Find z if both x and y are equal to 3. [E]

6. z varies directly as x and inversely as y. If $x = 1$ and $y = 11$, then $z = 3$. Find z if $x = 1$ and $y = 3$. [E]

7. z varies directly as x and inversely as the square of y. If both x and y are equal to 3, then $z = 6$. Find z if both x and y are equal to 6. [F]

8. z varies directly as the cube of x and inversely as the square of y. If both x and y are equal to 2, then $z = 40$. Find z if $x = 2$ and $y = 4$. [G]

9. z varies directly as x and inversely as the fourth power of y. If both x and $y = 2$, then $z = 1$. Find z if $x = 4$ and $y = 2$. [L]

10. z varies directly as the square of x and inversely as y. If $x = 8$ and $y = 8$, then $z = 8$. Find z if $x = 6$ and $y = 3$. [N]

11. z varies directly as the fourth power of x and inversely as the square of y. If $x = 2$ and $y = 16$, then $z = 1$. Find z if $x = 1$ and $y = 2$. [R]

12. z varies directly as the square of x and inversely as the cube of y. If $x = 2$ and $y = 1$, then $z = 28$. Find z if $x = 4$ and $y = 2$. [R]

13. z varies directly as the cube of x and inversely as the cube of y. If $x = 1$ and $y = 4$, then $z = 1$. Find z if $x = 2$ and $y = 4$. [W]

Enrichment 9-2

· ·

Understanding Horizontal Asymptotes

The graph of the function $y = \frac{3x + 5}{4x - 8}$ has the line $y = \frac{3}{4}$ as a
horizontal asymptote. By using long division, this function can be
rewritten in the form quotient + remainder: $y = \frac{3}{4} + \frac{11}{4x - 8}$.

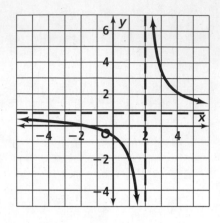

Examine what happens to the remainder and the value of y as the value of x
gets larger. Fill in the following table to four decimal places.

	x	$\frac{11}{4x - 8}$	$y = \frac{3}{4} + \frac{11}{4x - 8}$
1.	3		
2.	10		
3.	100		

Note that as x gets larger, the remainder gets smaller. So does the value of y.
Although the value of y is always greater than $\frac{3}{4}$, it gets closer to $\frac{3}{4}$ as x gets
larger. We say that as x gets infinitely large, y approaches $\frac{3}{4}$ from above.
We write: As $x \to +\infty$, $y \to \frac{3}{4}$ from above.

Examine what happens as x gets smaller. Fill in the following table to four
decimal places.

	x	$\frac{11}{4x - 8}$	$y = \frac{3}{4} + \frac{11}{4x - 8}$
4.	−3		
5.	−10		
6.	−100		

Here the value of y is always less than $\frac{3}{4}$, but it gets closer to $\frac{3}{4}$ as x gets
smaller (more negative). We write: As $x \to -\infty$, $y \to \frac{3}{4}$ from below.
In both cases, y approaches $\frac{3}{4}$, the horizontal asymptote.

Enrichment 9-3

Other Asymptotes

Recall that in a rational function if the degree of the numerator is more than the degree of the denominator, there is no horizontal asymptote. If, however, the degree of the numerator is exactly one more than the degree of its denominator, then the graph of the function has a **slant asymptote.**

We can use long division to find the equation of a slant asymptote. The equation of the slant asymptote is given by the quotient.

1. Use long division to find the slant asymptote of $f(x) = \dfrac{x^2 - x}{x + 1}$.

   The slant asymptote of the function is $y =$ _____.

2. Graph the slant asymptote on the axis to the right.

3. Graph the vertical asymptote for the equation in Exercise 1 on the axis to the right.

4. Complete the table, and plot the points accordingly.

x	-3	-2	0	2	3
$f(x)$					

   Connect with a smooth curve, being sure to draw near to all asymptotes.

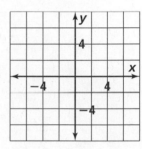

5. Use long division to find the slant asymptote of $f(x) = \dfrac{x^3}{x^2 + 1}$.

   The slant asymptote of the function is $y =$ _____.

6. Graph the slant asymptote on the axis to the right.

7. Find any vertical asymptotes for the equation in Exercise 5 and graph on the axis to the right.

8. Complete the table, and plot the points accordingly.

x	-3	-2	0	2	3
$f(x)$					

   Connect with a smooth curve, being sure to draw near to all asymptotes.

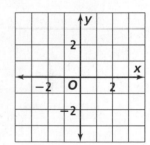

9. The technique used to find slant asymptotes works for rational functions in which the degree of the numerator is one more than the degree of the denominator. Use long division to find the asymptote of the rational function given by $f(x) = \dfrac{x^3 + 1}{x}$.

   The asymptote of the function is $y =$ _____.
   Can you guess the shape of this asymptote?

Enrichment 9-4

Saving Steps

Complete the tables below. Use a stopwatch to determine how long it takes to complete each answer.

Evaluate $\dfrac{x^2 - 5x + 6}{x^2 - 4x + 4}$.

Table 1

Value of x	Value of $\dfrac{x^2 - 5x + 6}{x^2 - 4x + 4}$	Time in Seconds
5		
10		
120		

Evaluate $\dfrac{x - 3}{x - 2}$.

Table 2

Value of x	Value of $\dfrac{x - 3}{x - 2}$	Time in Seconds
5		
10		
120		

Complete.

1. Compare both tables. What do you notice about the second column in each table? the last column?

2. How many separate operations did you do on the calculator for one evaluation in Table 1? in Table 2?

3. Simplify $\dfrac{x^2 - 8x + 7}{x^2 - 7x + 10} \div \dfrac{x^2 - 1}{x^2 - 4x + 4}$.

4. How many computational steps can be saved by using the simplified expression in Exercise 3 to evaluate the original expression?

Enrichment 9-5

The Superposition Principle

The illumination received from a light source is given by the formula

$$I = S \cdot D^{-2} \quad \text{or} \quad I = \frac{S}{D^2}$$

where I is the illumination at a certain point, S is the strength of the light source, measured in watts or kilowatts, and D is the distance of the point from the light source. The superposition principle states that the total illumination received at a given point is equal to the sum of the illuminations from each of the sources.

Suppose a plant is positioned at point A. Complete the following to find the total illumination received by the plant when both lights are on.

L1 = 100 watts	2 m A 3 m	L2 = 200 watts

$$I_{total} = I_{L1} + I_{L2}$$

$$= \frac{100}{2^2} + \frac{200}{\underline{\quad}}$$

$$= \underline{\hspace{2cm}}$$

$$= \underline{\hspace{2cm}} \qquad \text{Round to the nearest tenth.}$$

1. The amount of illumination received by the plant is _____.

Lighthouse A contains a 10-kilowatt light and is located on the shore of the ocean. Lighthouse B contains a 20-kilowatt light and is located 8 km out to sea from a point 6 km down the beach from Lighthouse A.

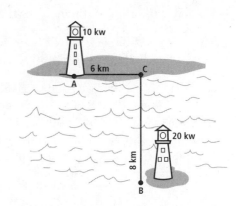

2. A man is x kilometers from lighthouse A. He is walking down the beach toward lighthouse B. What illumination does he receive as a function of x before he reaches point C?

3. Now suppose that the man is x kilometers beyond point C as he walks down the beach. What illumination does he receive as a function of x?

Enrichment 9-6

• •

Gravitational Attraction

Many physical phenomena obey inverse-square laws. That is, the strength of the quantity is inversely proportional to the square of the distance from the source.

Isaac Newton was the first to discover that gravity obeys an inverse-square law. The gravitational force F between objects of masses M and m separated by a distance D is given by $F = \frac{GMm}{D^2}$, where G is a constant.

Suppose that two stars, Alpha Major and Beta Minor, are separated by a distance of 6 light years. Alpha Major has four times the mass of Beta Minor. Let M represent the mass of Beta Minor. Suppose that an object of mass m is placed between the two stars at a distance of D light years from Beta Minor.

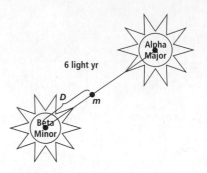

1. Write an expression for the gravitational force between this object and Beta Minor.

2. Write an expression for the gravitational force between this object and Alpha Major.

3. What is the distance of a neutral position of the object with mass m from Beta Minor? At neutral position, both Beta Minor and Alpha Major exert equal force on m.

A spaceship is floating on a line between a planet and its moon, experiencing an equal gravitational pull from each. When measurements are taken, it is determined that the craft is 300,000 km from the planet and 100,000 km from the moon.

4. What is the ratio of the mass of the planet to the mass of the moon?

5. What would be the ratio of their masses if the distance of the spaceship from the planet was R times the distance of the spaceship to the moon?

Once every 277 yr, the two moons of the planet Omega Minus line up in a straight line with the planet. The moons are equal in mass, and the inner moon is equidistant from the outer moon and from the planet. Measurements show that an object two thirds of the distance from the planet to the inner moon, and in the same line as all three, experiences an equal gravitational pull in both directions.

6. What is the ratio of the mass of the planet to the mass of one of its moons?

Enrichment 9-7

Probability Trees

Complex problems involving probability are often easier to visualize and solve using probability trees. For example, suppose that Alice, Bob, and Carol are running for president of the Math Club. Alice has a 0.45 probability of being elected, while Bob has 0.35 probability and Carol has a 0.2 probability of being elected. Sue and Ted are the candidates for vice president. If Alice becomes president, the probability is 0.7 that she will choose Sue as her vice president. If Bob becomes president, the probability that he will choose Sue is 0.4, while if Carol becomes president, the probability is 0.6 that she will choose Sue.

Examine the following tree diagram that represents the given information.

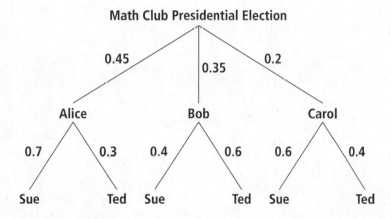

The probability that Alice will be elected president and choose Sue as her vice president can be found by multiplying the probabilities found along the "branches" of the tree. Thus, the Alice-Sue combination has a probability of $0.45 \times 0.7 = 0.315$ of occurring.

1. What is the probability of the Bob-Sue combination? _____ of Carol-Sue? _____

Use a tree diagram to compute the probabilities of each of the following events.

2. The probability that a random student at Elmville College is a freshman is 0.3; a sophomore, 0.25; and a junior or senior, 0.45. The probability that a freshman will major in engineering is 0.15; a sophomore, 0.2; and a junior or senior, 0.3. What is the probability that a random student at this college will major in engineering?

3. The Adams' restaurant specializes in beef, chicken, and seafood. Of its customers, 32% order beef and 41% order chicken. Of those who order beef, 73% also order dessert. Of those who order chicken, 62% also order dessert. If 65% of the customers order dessert, what is the probability that someone who orders seafood will also order dessert?

Chapter 9 Project: Under Pressure

Beginning the Chapter Project

Scuba diving helps marine scientists explore the underwater frontier. It is also a popular sport. But to dive safely, divers must understand that water pressure at depths of even 30 or 40 feet can be very dangerous.

Modern scuba-diving equipment allows divers to stay under water for long periods of time. But the depth and length of dives are limited by the amount of pressure that the human body can tolerate. You will use mathematics to explore safety issues related to scuba diving. Then, you will design a poster or brochure about scuba-diving safety.

List of Materials

- Calculator

- Graph paper

Activities

Activity 1: Graphing

Scuba divers must learn about pressure under water. At the water's surface, air exerts 1 atmosphere (atm) of pressure. Under water, the pressure increases. The pressure P (atm) varies with depth d (ft) according to the equation $P = \frac{d}{33} + 1$. Boyle's law states that the volume V of air varies inversely with the pressure P. If you hold your breath, the volume of air in your lungs increases as you ascend. If you have 4 qt of air in your lungs at a depth of 66 ft ($P = 3$ atm), the air will expand to 6 qt when you reach 33 ft, where $P = 2$ atm.

- Using the data in the example above, make a table and graph to show how the volume of air in your lungs varies with depth.

- Make a table and graph to show how the volume of air in your lungs varies with pressure.

Activity 2: Writing

In Activity 1, you found that the volume of air in a diver's lungs could more than double as the diver resurfaces. This expansion can cause the membranes of the lungs to rupture. Divers must learn to exhale properly while ascending.

- If you fill your lungs with 4 qt of air at a depth of 66 ft, how many quarts of air will you need to exhale during your ascent to still have 4 qt of air in your lungs when you reach the surface?

- Write an explanation of why beginning divers are told "Don't hold your breath!" Refer to your tables and graphs.

Chapter 9 Project (continued)

Activity 3: Solving

A popular size of scuba-diving tank is 71.2 ft^3 because this is the volume that the compressed air inside the tank would occupy at a normal surface pressure of 1 atm. The air in the tank is at a pressure of about 2250 lb/in.^{2}, so the tank itself can have a volume much less than 71.2 ft^3. How large does the tank need to be to hold 71.2 ft^3? (Hint: Use Boyle's Law: $PV = k$. Remember that 1 atm = 14.7 lb/in.^{2}.)

Activity 4: Solving

The rate at which a scuba diver uses air in the tank depends on many factors, such as the diver's age and lung capacity. Another important factor is the depth of the dive.

A scuba diver continues to breathe normally while descending. Every time the diver inhales, the tank delivers enough air to inflate the diver's lungs. This means that the amount of air delivered by the tank must increase with the depth in order to withstand the increasing pressure. At greater depths, the diver uses the air in the tank more quickly. The amount of time the air will last is inversely proportional to the pressure at the depth of the dive.

- Suppose a tank has enough air to last 60 min at the surface. How long will it last at a depth of 99 ft? (The pressure is 4 atm, or 4 times as great.)

- Make a table showing how long the air will last at 0 ft, 20 ft, 33 ft, 40 ft, 50 ft, 66 ft and 99 ft.

Finishing the Project

The questions in the activities should help you complete your project. Design a poster or brochure explaining what you learned about scuba-diving safety in this chapter. Use graphs, tables, and examples to support your conclusions.

Reflect and Revise

Work with a classmate to review your poster or brochure. Check that your graphs and examples are correct and that your explanations are clear. If necessary, refer to a book on scuba diving. Discuss your poster or brochure with an adult who works in the area of sports safety, such as a lifeguard, coach, physical education teacher, or recreation director. Ask for their suggestions for improvements.

Extending the Project

What other safety issues must scuba divers consider? Ask a scuba diver or refer to a book to find other things a scuba diver must consider to dive safely.

 **Take it to the NET** Visit PHSchool.com for information and links you might find helpful as you complete your project.

Chapter Project Manager

· ·

Chapter 9: Under Pressure

Getting Started

Read the project. As you work on the project, you will need a calculator, materials on which you can record your calculations, and materials to make accurate and attractive graphs. Keep all of your work for the project in a folder.

Checklist

❑ Activity 1: graphing air volume vs. depth and pressure

❑ Activity 2: understanding breathing while diving

❑ Activity 3: determining tank size

❑ Activity 4: determining duration of air supply

❑ project display

Suggestions

❑ Make a table and a graph for each comparison.

❑ Explain when and why divers must exhale.

❑ Use Boyle's Law.

❑ First, find the pressure at each depth.

❑ What visual aids might help someone viewing your project for the first time to understand lung capacity and its importance when scuba diving? What physical conditions of a diver might make a dive more dangerous than it would be otherwise?

Scoring Rubric

3 Calculations are correct. Graphs are neat, accurate, and clearly show the relationship between the variables. Explanations are clear and complete. The poster or brochure is clear and neat.

2 Calculations are mostly correct. Graphs are neat and mostly accurate with minor errors. Explanations are not complete.

1 Calculations contain both minor and major errors. Graphs are not accurate. Explanations and the poster or brochure are not clear or are incomplete.

0 Major elements of the project are incomplete or missing.

Your Evaluation of Project Evaluate your work, based on the *Scoring Rubric.*

Teacher's Evaluation of Project

Chapter Project Teacher Notes

Chapter 9: Under Pressure

About the Project
The Chapter Project gives students an opportunity to explore safety issues related to scuba diving. They use inverse proportions to find volumes of air in lungs and to find the sizes of tanks needed to hold enough air to dive to various depths.

Introducing the Project
- Ask students if they are familiar with the term – *the bends* – as it relates to diving. If a diver ascends too quickly, nitrogen bubbles form in the body which can cause a serious, potentially fatal condition called decompression sickness, frequently referred to as the bends.

- Ask students how they think a graph of the distance below the surface versus the volume of air in the lungs might look.

- Review the project with students and instruct students to make a list of questions they will need to answer to complete the project.

Activity 1: Graphing
Students make tables and graphs to find how the volume of air in their lungs varies with depth and pressure.

Activity 2: Writing
Students explain why they must exhale while ascending from driving.

Activity 3: Solving
Students use Boyle's Law to find how large a scuba diving tank needs to be.

Activity 4: Solving
Students use an inverse variation to find how long the air in a tank lasts at various depths.

Finishing the Project
You may wish to plan a project day on which students share their completed projects. Encourage students to explain their processes as well as their results. Ask students to review their project and update their folders.

- Ask students to review their methods for finding, recording, and solving formulas, and for making the tables and graphs used in the project.

- Ask groups to share their insights that resulted from completing the project, such as any shortcuts they found for solving formulas or making graphs.

Visit PHSchool.com for information, student links, and teacher support for this project.

✔ Checkpoint Quiz 1

Use with Lessons 9-1 through 9-3.

When $x = 2$ and $y = 3$, $z = 42$. Write the function that models each of the following relationships.

1. z varies inversely with x and directly with y.

2. z varies jointly with x and y.

3. z varies directly with x and inversely with the square of y.

Compare the graphs of the inverse variations.

4. $y = \frac{2}{x}$ and $y = -\frac{2}{x}$

5. $y = -\frac{1}{x}$ and $y = -\frac{1}{x} - 2$

6. $y = \frac{4}{x}$ and $y = \frac{4}{x + 2}$

7. $y = \frac{3}{x - 2} + 1$ and $y = \frac{3}{x + 2} - 1$

Sketch the graph of each rational function.

8. $y = \frac{x^2 - 4}{x + 2}$

9. $y = \frac{x - 1}{x + 2}$

10. $y = \frac{x^2 - x}{x - 1}$

11. $y = \frac{2x^2}{x^2 - x}$

- - - - ✂ -

✔ Checkpoint Quiz 2

Use with Lessons 9-4 through 9-5.

Simplify each expression.

1. $\frac{8x^2 - 10x + 3}{6x^2 + 3x - 3}$

2. $\frac{x^2 - 4}{x^2 - 1} \cdot \frac{x + 1}{x^2 + 2x}$

3. $\frac{7}{5y + 25} - \frac{4}{3y + 15}$

4. $\frac{x^2}{x^2 + 2x + 1} \div \frac{3x}{x^2 - 1}$

5. $\frac{2x + 4}{3x - 3} \cdot \frac{12x - 12}{x + 5}$

6. $\frac{7}{2xy^2} + \frac{3}{8x^2y}$

7. $\frac{x^2 - 16}{2x + 8} \div \frac{(x - 4)^2}{8x - 32}$

8. $5 - \frac{4x^2 - 5x + 1}{x^2 - x}$

9. $\frac{\frac{1}{3x}}{\frac{5}{6y}}$

10. $\frac{\frac{2}{y} - 1}{\frac{3}{x} + 1}$

Chapter Test

Chapter 9

Form A

Write a function that models each variation.

1. $x = -1$ when $y = 5$. y varies inversely as x.

2. $x = 3$ and $y = 12$ when $z = 2$. z varies directly with y and inversely with x.

Is the relationship between the values in each table a direct variation, an inverse variation, or neither? Write an equation to model any direct or inverse variation.

3.

x	−2	4	6
y	4	−8	−12

4.

x	−2	−1	3
y	$-\frac{1}{2}$	−1	$\frac{1}{3}$

Write an equation for the translation of $y = \frac{2}{x}$ with the given asymptotes.

5. $x = 1, y = -1$

6. $x = 5, y = \frac{1}{2}$

For each rational function, identify any holes or horizontal or vertical asymptotes of its graph.

7. $y = \frac{x}{x - 3}$

8. $y = \frac{-2(x - 8)}{(8 - x)}$

9. $y = \frac{(x + 3)}{(x + 2)(x + 3)}$

10. $y = \frac{x + 5}{(x - 2)(x - 3)}$

11. $y = \frac{1}{x + 4} - 3$

12. $y = \frac{3}{x - 1} - 2$

Sketch the graph of each rational function.

13. $y = \frac{x}{x(x - 2)}$

14. $y = \frac{1}{x + 4} - 3$

Simplify each rational expression. State any restrictions on the variable.

15. $\frac{3x^2 - 12}{x^2 - x - 6}$

16. $\frac{2x^2 - x}{4x^2 - 4x + 1} \div \frac{x^2}{8x - 4}$

Find the least common multiple of each pair of polynomials.

17. $x^2 - 16$ and $5x + 20$

18. $7(x - 2)(x + 5)$ and $2(x + 5)^2$

Simplify each sum or difference.

19. $\frac{2}{x + 5} + \frac{x}{x - 5}$

20. $\frac{3x}{x^2 - 4} - \frac{1}{x^2}$

21. $\frac{4(x + 3)}{(x - 1)(x + 2)} + \frac{(x - 2)(x + 3)}{(x - 1)}$

22. $\frac{3}{y^2 - 1} + \frac{y}{7y - 7}$

23. **Writing** Explain what it means for a rational expression to be in simplest form.

Chapter Test (continued)   Form A

Chapter 9

Simplify each complex fraction.

24. $\dfrac{1 + \frac{2}{3}}{\frac{3}{4} - \frac{1}{3}}$

25. $\dfrac{1 + \frac{1}{x}}{5 - \frac{1}{y}}$

Solve each equation. Check each solution.

26. $\dfrac{x}{3} + \dfrac{x}{2} = 10$

27. $\dfrac{y - 3}{5} = \dfrac{y + 1}{7}$

28. $\dfrac{x}{2} = 2x - 3$

29. $-\dfrac{x}{4} = \dfrac{2x}{3}$

30. $\dfrac{1}{x} - \dfrac{1}{6} = \dfrac{4}{3x^2}$

31. $\dfrac{2x - 4}{x - 5} = 0$

32. Open-Ended Write a rational equation that can be solved using cross products. Solve the equation.

33. Chad can paint a room in 2 h. Cassie can paint a room in 3 h. How long would it take them to paint a room working together?

A spinner is spun. State whether the events are mutually exclusive. Then find *P(A or B)*.

34. *A* = an even number
   B = a number ≤ 3

35. *A* = an odd number
   B = a multiple of 2

36. *A* = a number < 3
   B = a multiple of 3

37. Suppose you have a CD which contains a compilation of songs. Eight songs can be classified as rock, three as blues, and two as jazz. Today you hit the shuffle button on your CD player, which plays the songs in a random order. Tomorrow you do the same thing. What is the probability that the CD player plays a blues song first each day?

Chapter Test

Chapter 9

Form B

Write a function that models each variation.

1. $x = -4$ when $y = 2$. y varies inversely as x.

2. $x = 24$ and $y = 3$ when $z = 2$. z varies directly with x and inversely with y.

Is the relationship between the values in the table a direct variation, an inverse variation, or neither? Write an equation to model any direct or inverse variation.

3.

x	-2	1	3
y	-8	4	12

4.

x	-6	2	8
y	$\frac{1}{3}$	-1	$-\frac{1}{4}$

Write an equation for the translation of $y = \frac{4}{x}$ with the given asymptotes.

5. $x = -2, y = -1$

6. $x = \frac{1}{3}, y = 2$

For each rational function, identify any holes or horizontal or vertical asymptotes of its graph.

7. $y = \dfrac{2x}{x + 4}$

8. $y = \dfrac{-6(7 - x)}{(x - 7)}$

9. $y = \dfrac{(x - 4)}{(x - 4)(x + 9)}$

10. $y = \dfrac{x - 7}{(x - 4)(x + 4)}$

11. $y = \dfrac{1}{x + 2} + 3$

12. $y = \dfrac{1}{x - 5} - 1$

Sketch the graph of each rational function.

13. $y = \dfrac{x}{x(x + 3)}$

14. $y = \dfrac{2}{x - 1} + 4$

Simplify each rational expression. State any restrictions on the variable.

15. $\dfrac{x^2 - 7x}{14 - 2x}$

16. $\dfrac{2x - 10}{3x - 21} \div \dfrac{x - 5}{4x - 28}$

Find the least common multiple of each pair of polynomials.

17. $x^2 - 25$ and $3x + 15$

18. $8(x + 6)(x - 3)$ and $2(x + 6)^2$

Simplify each sum or difference.

19. $\dfrac{3}{x + 4} + \dfrac{x}{x - 4}$

20. $\dfrac{2x}{x^2 - 9} - \dfrac{1}{x^2}$

21. $\dfrac{5}{x^2 - 36} - \dfrac{9}{x^2 + 5x - 6}$

22. $\dfrac{5}{y^2 - 16} + \dfrac{y}{3y - 12}$

23. Writing Explain how to tell whether a rational function has a removable discontinuity.

Chapter Test (continued)   **Form B**

Chapter 9

Simplify each complex fraction.

24. $\dfrac{2 - \frac{4}{3}}{\frac{1}{2} + \frac{1}{6}}$

25. $\dfrac{2 - \frac{1}{x}}{3 + \frac{1}{y}}$

Solve each equation. Check each solution.

26. $\dfrac{2}{x} + \dfrac{2}{2x} = 3$

27. $\dfrac{4}{x} = \dfrac{x}{x + 3}$

28. $\dfrac{x}{4} = 3x + 1$

29. $\dfrac{x}{3} = \dfrac{4x}{5}$

30. $\dfrac{1}{x} + \dfrac{1}{2} = \dfrac{3}{2x^2}$

31. $\dfrac{3x - 12}{x - 7} = 0$

32. **Open-Ended** Write a rational equation that can be solved using common denominators. Solve the equation you write.

33. Brandon can clean the garage in 4 h. Ashley can clean the garage in 3 h. How long would it take them to clean the garage working together?

A spinner is spun. State whether the events are mutually exclusive. Then find *P(A or B)*.

34. A = an odd number
B = a number ≥ 6

35. A = an odd number
B = an even number

36. A = a number > 4
B = a number < 3

37. Suppose you have a CD which contains a compilation of songs. Six songs can be classified as rock, two as alternative rock, and four as blues. Today you hit the shuffle button on your CD player, which plays the songs in a random order. Tomorrow you do the same thing. What is the probability that the CD player plays an alternative song first each day?

Alternative Assessment

Form C

Chapter 9

Give complete answers.

TASK 1

   a. Write a function that shows an inverse variation situation.

   b. Find the constant of the inverse variation.

   c. Determine the dependent and independent variables.

   d. Identify the domain and range.

   e. Find the values of any asymptotes.

   f. Graph the function, making sure to indicate any asymptotes.

TASK 2

Use the function you wrote in Task 1 to answer each question.

   a. Let the dependent variable be 3. Find the value of the independent variable.

   b. Let the independent variable be 6. Find the value of the dependent variable.

   c. What value does the dependent variable approach when the independent variable approaches infinity?

   d. What value does the independent variable approach when the dependent variable approaches infinity?

Alternative Assessment (continued)   Form C

Chapter 9

TASK 3

Use the function $t(r) = \frac{d}{r}$, where t is the time in hours, d is the distance in miles, and r is the rate in miles per hour to answer each question.

   a. Sydney drives 10 mi at a certain rate and then drives 20 additional miles at a rate 5 mi/h faster than the first rate. Write algebraic expressions for the time along each part of Sydney's trip. Add these times to determine an algebraic equation for the total time in terms of the initial rate, $t_{Total}(r)$.

   b. Determine the reasonable domain and range and describe any discontinuities of $t_{Total}(r)$.
Graph $t_{Total}(r)$ using your graphing calculator.

   c. At approximately what rate, to the nearest mile per hour, must Sydney drive if the entire 30 mi must be covered in about 45 min? Find the answer using the graph and using algebraic methods.

   d. How long will it take Sydney to drive the entire 30 mi if the car's rate varies between 10 and 20 mi/h? Use the graph and algebraic methods to find the answer.

TASK 4

Six overhead lights are evaluated to find the intensity of light at work stations that are about 2 m from the light. Use the set of data shown below. Round to the nearest percent, if necessary.

Trial Number	1	2	3	4	5	6
Intensity of Light (lux)	102	99	105	97	100	98
Distance from the Light (m)	2.1	2.0	1.7	2.2	2.1	1.9

   a. What is the probability that a light used in the experiment and chosen at random is more than 2 m from a work station? less than 2 m from a work station? What is the probability that a light used in the experiment and chosen at random has an intensity of more than 100 lux? less than 99 lux?

   b. What is the probability that a light used in the experiment and chosen at random is more than 2 m from a work station and has an intensity of more than 100 lux. Use your answers from part **a** to find this result. Are these two events independent, dependent, or mutually exclusive?

   c. What is the probability that a light used in the experiment and chosen at random is more than 100 lux or less than 99 lux? Use your answers from part **a** to find this result. Arc these two events independent, dependent, or mutually exclusive?

Name _____ Class _____ Date _____

Cumulative Review

Chapters 1–9

For Exercises 1–12, choose the correct letter.

1. Find $\begin{bmatrix} 3 & 2 \\ 0 & -1 \end{bmatrix}\begin{bmatrix} 3 & -1 \\ 0 & 2 \end{bmatrix}$.

   A. $\begin{bmatrix} 3 & -2 \\ 0 & -2 \end{bmatrix}$ **B.** $\begin{bmatrix} 4 & 1 \\ 0 & 1 \end{bmatrix}$ **C.** $\begin{bmatrix} 0 & 2 \\ 0 & 0 \end{bmatrix}$ **D.** $\begin{bmatrix} 9 & 1 \\ 0 & -2 \end{bmatrix}$

2. Which point lies on the graph of $2x + y - z = 3$?

   A. $(3, 0, -2)$ **B.** $(0, 1, -2)$ **C.** $(1, 0, 0)$ **D.** $(0, 0, 3)$

3. Which of these trend lines is correct?

   A. 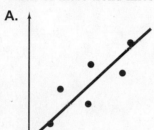   **B.**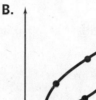

   C. 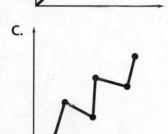   **D.**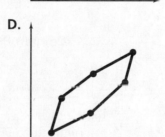

4. Which of these is a binomial quadratic?

   A. $4x^2 + 6$ **B.** $x^2 + 3x - 2$ **C.** $2x^2 + 2x + 2$ **D.** $x^3 - 2x^2$

5. Find the inverse of $y = 6x - 2$.

   A. $y = \frac{1}{6}x - \frac{1}{2}$ **B.** $y = 6x + 2$ **C.** $y = \frac{1}{6}x + \frac{1}{3}$ **D.** $y = \frac{1}{6}x + 2$

6. Evaluate $_{15}C_3$.

   A. 216   **B.** 144   **C.** 455   **D.** 227

7. Simplify $\log_2 2 + (\log_2 20 - \log_2 5)$.

   A. $\log_2 17$ **B.** 3   **C.** $\log_2 6$ **D.** 4

8. Which matrix contains $a_{21} = 4$?

   A. $\begin{bmatrix} -4 & -4 \\ 4 & -4 \end{bmatrix}$ **B.** $\begin{bmatrix} -4 & -4 \\ -4 & 4 \end{bmatrix}$ **C.** $\begin{bmatrix} -4 & 4 \\ -4 & -4 \end{bmatrix}$ **D.** $\begin{bmatrix} 4 & -4 \\ -4 & -4 \end{bmatrix}$

9. Which point cannot be on the line $y = 2x + 5$?

   A. $(-4, -3)$ **B.** $(3, 11)$ **C.** $(1, 7)$ **D.** $(0, 6)$

Cumulative Review (continued)

Chapters 1–9

10. To which set of numbers does 15 not belong?

    A. rational numbers   **B.** integers   **C.** whole numbers   **D.** irrational numbers

11. Which of these is equal to $\log_8 5 - \log_8 3$?

    A. $\log_3 5$ **B.** $\log_8 2$ **C.** $\log_8 \frac{5}{3}$ **D.** e^2

12. Which system has no solution?

    A. $\begin{cases} y = 2x + 3 \\ y = 3x + 2 \end{cases}$ **B.** $\begin{cases} y = 4x + 3 \\ y = 4x - 3 \end{cases}$ **C.** $\begin{cases} y = \frac{1}{2}x \\ y = \frac{1}{20}x \end{cases}$ **D.** $\begin{cases} y > 3 \\ x < 2 \end{cases}$

Compare the quantity in Column A with that in Column B. Choose the best answer.

    A. The quantity in Column A is greater.

    B. The quantity in Column B is greater.

    C. The two quantities are equal.

    D. The relationship cannot be determined on the basis of the information supplied.

	Column A	Column B
13.	i^2	i^4
14.	constant of variation for the inverse variation containing the point (4, 3)	constant of variation for the inverse variation containing the point (6, 2)

A jar contains three green marbles and five white marbles. Suppose you choose a marble at random, and do not replace it. Then you choose a second marble. Find the probability of each event.

15. You select a green marble then a white marble.

16. Both of the marbles you select are green.

Find each answer.

17. Write the equation of a direct variation that includes the point (2, 6).

18. **Open-Ended** Describe two mutually exclusive events.

19. **Writing** Explain how to determine the equation of the horizontal asymptote for the graph of a rational function.

Chapter 9 Answers

Practice 9-1

1. 1 **2.** 1.2 **3.** 50 **4.** $\frac{2}{7}$ **5.** 4.2 **6.** $y = \frac{14}{x}$ **7.** $y = \frac{36}{x}$

8. $y = -\frac{24}{x}$ **9.** $y = -\frac{30}{x}$ **10.** $y = \frac{0.8}{x}$ or $y = \frac{4}{5x}$

11. $y = \frac{8}{x}$ **12.** $y = \frac{3}{x}$ **13.** $y = \frac{6.3}{x}$ or $y = \frac{63}{10x}$

14. $y = -\frac{0.3}{x}$ or $y = -\frac{3}{10x}$ **15.** I varies inversely with R.
16. A varies jointly with b and h. **17.** h varies directly with V
and inversely with B. **18.** V varies directly with the cube of r.
19. $\frac{4}{3}$ **20.** -4 **21.** 2 **22.** $y = \frac{8}{x}$; 1 **23.** $y = -\frac{1}{x}$; $-\frac{1}{8}$

24. $y = \frac{7.2}{x}$ or $y = \frac{36}{5x}$; 0.9 **25.** $z = 2xy$; 48

26. $z = \frac{3x}{y^3}$; $\frac{9}{32}$ **27.** inverse; $y = \frac{20}{x}$ **28.** neither

29. direct; $y = 6x$ **30.** direct; $y = 125x$ **31.** neither

32. inverse; $y = \frac{15}{x}$

Practice 9-2

1. $y = -\frac{3}{x - 2} + 1$ **2.** $y = -\frac{3}{x + 1} + 3$

3. $y = -\frac{3}{x - 4} - 2$ **4.** $y = -\frac{3}{x} + 6$ **5.** $y = -\frac{3}{x - 3}$

6. $y = -\frac{3}{x - 1} + 2$ **7.** $y = -\frac{3}{x + 3} - 1$

8. $y = -\frac{3}{x + 2} + 1$

9.
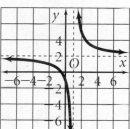
$; x = 1, y = 2$

10.
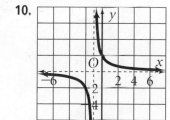
$; x = -1, y = 0$

11.
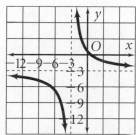
$; x = -3, y = -3$

12.
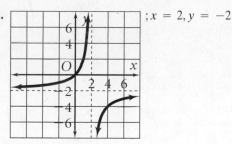
$; x = 2, y = -2$

13.
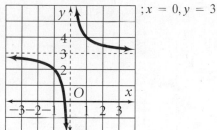
$; x = 0, y = 3$

14.
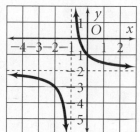
$; x = -1, y = -2$

15.
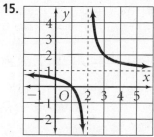
$; x = 2, y = 1$

16.
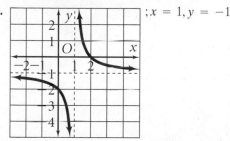
$; x = 1, y = -1$

Chapter 9 Answers (continued)

17. 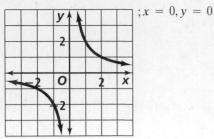 $; x = 0, y = 0$

22. 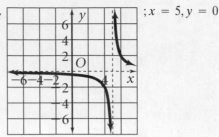 $; x = 5, y = 0$

18. 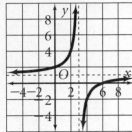 $; x = 3, y = 1$

23. 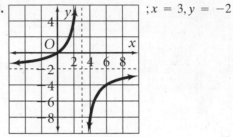 $; x = 3, y = -2$

19. 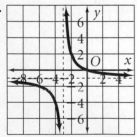 $; x = -1, y = 2$

24. 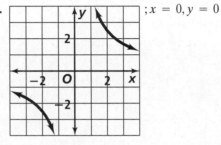 $; x = 0, y = 0$

20. 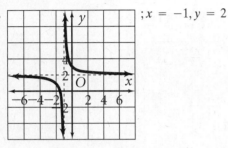 $; x = 0, y = 0.5$

25. 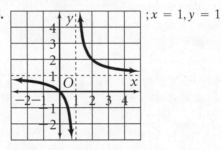 $; x = 1, y = 1$

21. 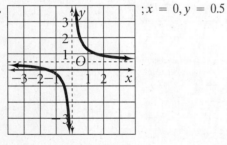 $; x = -3, y = -1$

26. 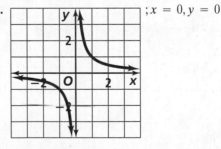 $; x = 0, y = 0$

27. 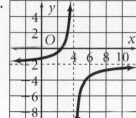 ; $x = 4, y = -2$

28. 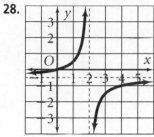 ; $x = 2, y = -0.5$

29. 2.25 ft **30.** 412.5 Hz **31.** 825 Hz **32.** 165 Hz **33.** $7.50
34. 324 keepsakes **35.** $4.50 **36.** $36.00 **37.** Answers may
vary. Sample: The axes are asymptotes for both graphs; both
are symmetric with respect to $y = x$ and $y = -x$; the
branches of $y = \frac{1}{x}$ are closer to the axes than are the
branches of $y = \frac{5}{x}$. **38.** Answers may vary. Sample: The axes
are asymptotes for both graphs; both are symmetric with
respect to $y = x$ and $y = -x$; the y-axis is a line of reflection
of the two graphs. **39.** Answers may vary. Sample: The axes
are asymptotes for both graphs; both are symmetric with
respect to $y = x$ and $y = -x$; the branches of $y = \frac{2}{x}$ are
closer to the axes than are the branches of $y = \frac{20}{x}$.
40. Answers may vary. Sample: The axes are asymptotes for
both graphs; both are symmetric with respect to $y = x$ and $y
= -x$; the branches of $y = -\frac{1}{x}$ are closer to the axes than
are the branches of $y = -\frac{10}{x}$. **41.** Answers may vary.
Sample: The axes are asymptotes for both graphs; both are
symmetric with respect to $y = x$ and $y = -x$; the y-axis is a
line of reflection of the two graphs. **42.** Answers may vary.
Sample: The axes are asymptotes for both graphs; both are
symmetric with respect to $y = x$ and $y = -x$; the branches
of $y = \frac{0.02}{x}$ are closer to the axes than are the branches of
$y = \frac{0.2}{x}$.

Practice 9-3

1. $-3, 4$ **2.** ± 2 **3.** 2 **4.** $0, -2$ **5.** -1 **6.** $0, \pm 3$ **7.** $y = 0$
8. $y = 1$ **9.** $y = \frac{1}{2}$ **10.** $y = 2$ **11.** $y = 0$ **12.** $y = 1.5$

13. 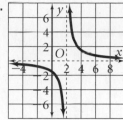 **14.**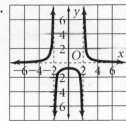

15. 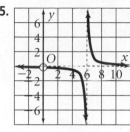 **16.**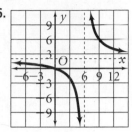

17. 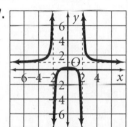 **18.**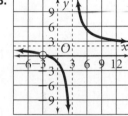

19. 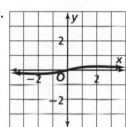 **20.**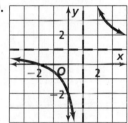

21.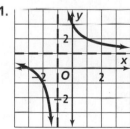

22. vertical asymptote at $x = -2$; hole at $x = 2$
23. vertical asymptote at $x = 1$; hole at $x = 0$ **24.** vertical
asymptotes at $x = 1$ and $x = -1$ **25.** vertical asymptote at
$x = -2$ **26.** no vertical asymptotes or holes **27.** vertical
asymptote at $x = 3$; hole at $x = -3$ **28.** vertical asymptote
at $x = 4$ **29.** vertical asymptotes at $x = -\frac{4}{5}$ and $x = 3$
30. vertical asymptotes at $x = 2$ and $x = -2$

31a. $y = \dfrac{0.02x + 3500}{x}$, where $x = $ number of pages;

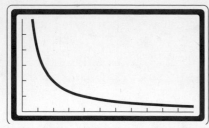

31b. at least 2365 pages **31c.** 3571 pages **31d.** 7292 pages
31e. $x = 0; y = 0.02$

Practice 9-4

1. $\dfrac{2x + 1}{x}; x \neq 0$ **2.** $2; x \neq -\dfrac{3}{2}$ **3.** $3; y \neq 1$ or -1

4. $\dfrac{4}{3}; x \neq -5$ **5.** $\dfrac{x + 1}{x + 2}; x \neq 0$ or -2 **6.** $\dfrac{3}{5}; x \neq -2$

7. $\dfrac{2}{y + 6}; y \neq 0$ or -6 **8.** $\dfrac{x}{x + 5}; x \neq 5$ or -5

9. $\dfrac{x - 3}{x - 6}; x \neq 6$ or -6 **10.** $\dfrac{x + 8}{x - 7}; x \neq 7$ or -5

11. $\dfrac{3x - 6}{x - 3}; x \neq 3$ or -2 **12.** $\dfrac{4x - 12}{x + 7}; x \neq -3$ or -7

13. $\dfrac{2x + 1}{3x + 2}; x \neq -5$ or $-\dfrac{2}{3}$ **14.** $\dfrac{2x + 3}{x - 1}; x \neq 1$ or $\dfrac{2}{3}$

15. $\dfrac{7}{x + 4}; x \neq 4$ or -4 **16.** $\dfrac{x - 3}{2}; x \neq -3$

17. $10; a \neq -1, 0$ **18.** $-1; x \neq -\dfrac{2}{5}, 0, \pm 3$

19. $x^2 - 1; x \neq -4, 2$ **20.** $x + 3; x \neq -4, -3, -1$

21. $\dfrac{7y - 28}{6y + 24}; y \neq -5, -4$ **22.** $\dfrac{3x^2 + 3x}{x - 5}; x \neq 0, \pm 5$

23. $\dfrac{5y^2 + 10y + 5}{36y + 72}; y \neq -2, -1$ **24.** $\dfrac{3x - 6}{14}; x \neq -1, 2$

25. $\dfrac{y}{y - 2}; y \neq 2, \pm 9$ **26.** $\dfrac{3}{2}; y \neq \pm 6$ **27.** $\dfrac{y}{5}; y \neq 0, \pm 7$

28. $\dfrac{x + 2}{x - 2}; x \neq \dfrac{1}{2}, 2, 3, 5$ **29.** $\dfrac{x^2 - 16}{x^2 - 9}; x \neq \pm 1, \pm 3$

30. $1; x \neq -3, 0, 5$ **31.** $\dfrac{x^2 - 5x + 6}{x^2 + 5x + 6}; x \neq -3, -2$

32. $\dfrac{1}{x}; x \neq 0, \pm 6$ **33.** $x + 8; x \neq -2, \pm 8$ **34.** $\dfrac{4}{y}; x, y \neq 0$

35. $\dfrac{4x - 16}{3x}; x \neq 0, \dfrac{1}{3}, 5, \pm 4$ **36.** $\dfrac{x^3}{6y}; x, y \neq 0$

37. $3x; x \neq 0, -2$ **38.** $\dfrac{x}{3}; x \neq -6, -4, 2$

39. $\dfrac{x^2 - 2x + 1}{x^2 + 14x + 49}; x \neq -7, -3, 4$

40. $\dfrac{x^2 + 2x + 1}{x^2 + x - 2}; x \neq -2, \pm 1$

Practice 9-5

1. $6x(x + 2)(2x - 3)$ **2.** $6(x - 1)(x - 2)^2(x + 10)$

3. $(2x + 3)^2(2x - 3)$ **4.** $10x(x + 3)^2(x - 3)$ **5.** $\dfrac{2x^2}{5}$

6. $\dfrac{x^2 + 2x - 2}{12}$ **7.** $\dfrac{3}{xy^3}$ **8.** $\dfrac{2 - n}{n - 4}$ **9.** $-\dfrac{x}{9}$

10. $\dfrac{7y + 5}{3y}$ **11.** $\dfrac{3(3y - 1)}{y^2 - 5}$ **12.** $\dfrac{12y + 5x}{10x^2y^2}$

13. $\dfrac{3 - 2x^2y^2}{8x^3y^3}$ **14.** $\dfrac{10x - 26}{(x + 5)(x - 5)(x + 1)}$

15. $\dfrac{9y + 4x}{21x^2y^2}$ **16.** $\dfrac{x^2y}{x^2 - 4}$ **17.** $\dfrac{3}{x + 2}$

18. $\dfrac{(5x + 1)(x + 3)}{(x - 3)(x + 2)(x + 5)(x + 1)}$

19. $\dfrac{7x + 5}{2(3x - 1)(2x - 3)(2x + 3)}$ **20.** $\dfrac{2(x + 2)}{x(x - 3)}$

21. $\dfrac{4x + 1}{(x + 5)(x + 1)(x - 2)}$ **22.** $\dfrac{4x^2 - 36x + 3}{x - 9}$

23. $\dfrac{3x^2 + 14}{x^2 + 5}$ **24.** $\dfrac{5x^2 - 25x + 31}{x^2 - 5x + 6}$ **25.** $\dfrac{5x + 6}{3x - 1}$

26. $\dfrac{5a^2 + 2a}{a^2 - 4}$ **27.** $\dfrac{8c^2}{c^2 - 9}$ **28.** $\dfrac{2}{gh}$ **29.** $-\dfrac{6t}{t^2 - 25}$

30. $\dfrac{8r^2}{r^2 - 4}$ **31.** $\dfrac{x^2 + y^2}{x^2 + xy}$ **32.** $\dfrac{2y}{3x}$ **33.** $\dfrac{x + 2}{4x - 6}$

34. $\dfrac{x}{2x^2 - 3x - 2}$ **35.** $\dfrac{y - 2}{4y}$ **36.** $\dfrac{15}{4}$ **37.** $2x + 3$

38. $\dfrac{3x - 3}{5x + 5}$ **39.** $\dfrac{2y + 6xy}{x}$ **40.** $\dfrac{3y(y - 2)}{(y - 6)(y + 2)(y - 4)}$

41a. $\dfrac{24}{17}$ ohms **41b.** $\dfrac{4}{3}$ ohms

Practice 9-6

1. ± 3 **2.** ± 4 **3.** $-\dfrac{4}{11}$ **4.** $-\dfrac{9}{17}$ **5.** $\dfrac{9}{4}$ **6.** -2 **7.** -0.2

8. -0.5 **9.** 3 **10.** -2 **11.** 0 **12.** -17 **13.** 12 **14.** 6

15. $\dfrac{3}{16}$ **16.** no solution **17.** -9 **18.** 7 **19.** 11 **20.** 41

21. 5 **22.** -3 **23.** 0 **24.** $-\dfrac{19}{25}$ **25.** -3 **26.** 18 **27.** $\dfrac{60}{7}$

28. -5 **29.** no solution **30.** 12 **31.** 4 **32.** $\dfrac{14}{3}$

33. no solution **34.** 6 **35.** -5 **36.** -1

37. about 13 mi/h tail wind **38.** about 14 mi/h head wind

39. about 1.3 days **40.** Tom: 125 min, Huck: 500 min

Practice 9-7

1. no **2.** yes **3.** yes **4.** no **5.** dependent **6.** independent
7. independent **8.** dependent **9.** 20% **10a.** 0.6 **10b.** 1
10c. 0.7 **10d.** 0.6 **11a.** $\dfrac{2}{3}$ **11b.** $\dfrac{2}{3}$ **11c.** $\dfrac{2}{3}$ **11d.** $\dfrac{1}{6}$

12. about 69.6% **13.** 12.5% **14.** $\dfrac{1}{20}$ **15.** 0.16 **16.** $\dfrac{1}{20}$

17. $\dfrac{11}{12}$ **18.** 55% **19.** 38%

Reteaching 9-1

1. 3.5 h **2.** 5 h **3.** about 28 items **4.** 6.75 cm

Reteaching 9-2

1. 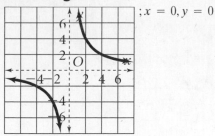 $; x = 0, y = 0$

2. 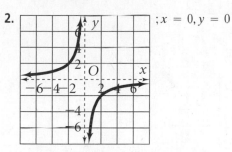 $; x = 0, y = 0$

3. 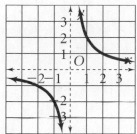 $; x = 0, y = 0$

4. 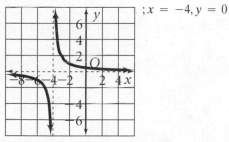 $; x = -4, y = 0$

5. 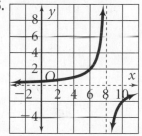 $; x = 8, y = 0$

6. 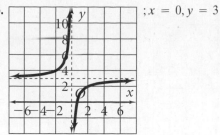 $; x = 0, y = 3$

7. 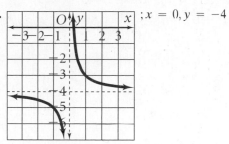 $; x = 0, y = -4$

8. 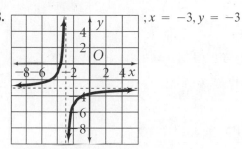 $; x = -3, y = -3$

9. 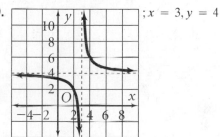 $; x = 3, y = 4$

10. 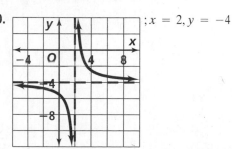 $; x = 2, y = -4$

11. 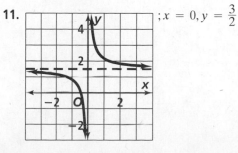 $; x = 0, y = \frac{3}{2}$

12.
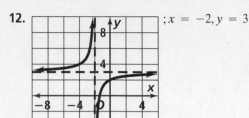 $; x = -2, y = 3$

Reteaching 9-3
1. asymptotes at $x = 3$ and -3 **2.** asymptote at $x = 0$
3. asymptote at $x = 1$ **4.** asymptotes at $x = 1$ and -5
5. asymptote at $x = -1$ **6.** asymptote at $x = 0$
7. asymptote at $x = 0$ and hole at $x = -2$ **8.** asymptote at
$x = -2$ and hole at $x = -1$ **9.** asymptote at $x = 3$ and
hole at $x = -1$

Reteaching 9-4
1. $\dfrac{1}{x - y}$ **2.** $\dfrac{a + 2}{a - 5}$ **3.** $\dfrac{3x - 12}{2x + 8}$ **4.** $\dfrac{2}{3}$ **5.** $x - 2$
6. $\dfrac{1 - x}{4x^2 + 16x}$ **7.** 5 **8.** $\dfrac{1}{x^2 + 4x + 4}$ **9.** $\dfrac{8}{3}$ **10.** $\dfrac{x - 7}{x^2}$
11. $\dfrac{x - 2}{x}$ **12.** $\dfrac{x + 2}{3x - 6}$ **13.** $\dfrac{3}{x}$ **14.** $\dfrac{3x + 6}{2x + 6}$ **15.** 3 **16.** $\dfrac{1}{x^4}$

Reteaching 9-5
1. 1 **2.** $\dfrac{y - 2}{y - 1}$ **3.** $\dfrac{3x - 4}{(x + 2)(x - 2)}$ **4.** $\dfrac{3y - 10}{(y - 5)(y + 4)}$
5. $\dfrac{x - 3}{(x + 1)(x + 3)}$ **6.** $\dfrac{x - 5}{(x + 2)(x - 2)}$ **7.** $-\dfrac{43}{28x}$
8. $\dfrac{12x^2 - x - 39}{3(x + 11)}$ **9.** $\dfrac{4x^2 - 3x + 15}{x^2(x + 3)(x - 2)}$

Reteaching 9-6
1. $\dfrac{3}{4}$ **2.** $5, -\dfrac{3}{2}$ **3.** $\dfrac{8}{5}$ **4.** 6 **5.** -5 **6.** 4 **7.** $\dfrac{3}{2}, \dfrac{8}{3}$
8. no solution **9.** 1 **10.** 0.5 **11.** -0.5 **12.** 25
13. Quinn: 3.75 h, Jack: 15 h

Reteaching 9-7
1. $\dfrac{7}{10}$ **2.** $\dfrac{7}{15}$ **3.** $\dfrac{37}{45}$

Enrichment 9-1
ALFRED WEGENER
1. 1 **2.** 6 **3.** 13 **4.** 5 **5.** 9 **6.** 11 **7.** 3 **8.** 10 **9.** 2 **10.** 12
11. 4 **12.** 14 **13.** 8

Enrichment 9-2
1. 2.7500; 3.5000 **2.** 0.3438; 1.0938 **3.** 0.0281; 0.7781
4. -0.5500; 0.2000 **5.** -0.2292; 0.5208 **6.** -0.0270; 0.7230

Enrichment 9-3
1. $x - 2$
2.–4.
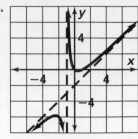

4. $-6; -6; 0; \dfrac{2}{3}; \dfrac{3}{2}$ **5.** x

6.–8.
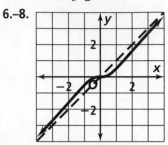

8. $-\dfrac{27}{10}; -\dfrac{8}{5}; 0; \dfrac{8}{5}, \dfrac{27}{10}$ **9.** x^2; parabola

Enrichment 9-4
$\dfrac{2}{3}, \dfrac{7}{8}, \dfrac{117}{118} \cdots$
$\dfrac{2}{3}, \dfrac{7}{8}, \dfrac{117}{118} \cdots$

1. The second columns are exactly the same; it took less time
to complete Table 2. **2.** 9; 3
3. $\dfrac{(x - 7)(x - 2)}{(x - 5)(x + 1)}$ **4.** 10

Enrichment 9-5
$3^2; 25 + 22.\overline{2}; 47.2$
1. about 47.2 watts/m² **2.** $\dfrac{30x^2 - 120x + 1000}{x^2(x^2 - 12x + 100)}$
3. $\dfrac{30x^2 + 240x + 1360}{(x^2 + 12x + 36)(x^2 + 64)}$

Enrichment 9-6
1. $\dfrac{GMm}{D^2}$ **2.** $\dfrac{4\,GMm}{(6 - D)^2}$ **3.** 2 light yr **4.** $9 : 1$ **5.** $R^2 : 1$
6. $17 : 4$

Enrichment 9-7
1. 0.14; 0.12 **2.** 0.23 **3.** about 0.60

Chapter 9 Answers (continued)

Chapter Project

Activity 1: Graphing

Depth (ft)	Volume (qt)
0	12
33	6
66	4
99	3
132	2.4
165	2

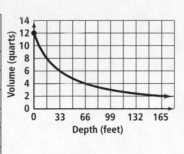

Pressure (atm)	Volume (qt)
1	12
2	6
3	4
4	3
5	2.4
6	2

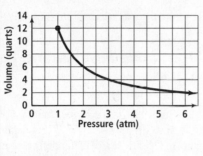

Activity 2: Writing
8 qt; Answers may vary. Sample: Divers must exhale during ascent to prevent the expanding air in their lungs from damaging their lungs.

Activity 3: Solving
0.465 ft^3

Activity 4: Solving
15 min

Depth (ft)	Pressure (atm) to the nearest hundredth	Time (min) to the nearest tenth
0	1.00	60.0
20	1.61	37.3
33	2.00	30.0
40	2.21	27.1
50	2.51	23.9
66	3.00	20.0
99	4.00	15.0

✔ Checkpoint Quiz 1

1. $z = \frac{28y}{x}$ **2.** $z = 7xy$ **3.** $z = \frac{189x}{y^2}$

4. Answers may vary. Sample: The axes are asymptotes for both graphs; both are symmetric with respect to $y = x$ and $y = -x$; the y-axis is a line of reflection of the two graphs.

5. Answers may vary. Sample: The vertical asymptotes of the graphs are $x = 0$ for both; the horizontal asymptotes are $y = 0$ and $y = -2$, respectively; the graph of $y = -\frac{1}{x} - 2$ is a translation of the graph of $y = -\frac{1}{x}$. **6.** Answers may vary. Sample: The vertical asymptotes are $x = 0$ and $x = -2$, respectively; the horizontal asymptotes are $y = 0$ for both graphs; the graph of $y = \frac{4}{x + 2}$ is a translation of the graph of $y = \frac{4}{x}$. **7.** Answers may vary. Sample: The vertical asymptotes are $x = 2$ and $x = -2$, respectively; the horizontal asymptotes are $y = 1$ and $y = -1$, respectively; each graph is a translation of the graph of $y = \frac{3}{x}$.

8.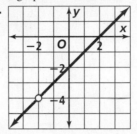

9.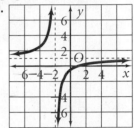

10.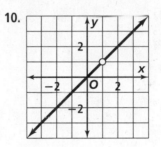

11.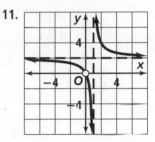

✔ Checkpoint Quiz 2

1. $\frac{4x - 3}{3x + 3}$ **2.** $\frac{x - 2}{x(x - 1)}$ **3.** $\frac{1}{15(y + 5)}$ **4.** $\frac{x(x - 1)}{3(x + 1)}$

5. $\frac{8(x + 2)}{x + 5}$ **6.** $\frac{28x + 3y}{8x^2y^2}$ **7.** 4 **8.** $\frac{x + 1}{x}$ **9.** $\frac{2y}{5x}$

10. $\frac{2x - xy}{3y + xy}$

Chapter Test, Form A

1. $y = -\frac{5}{x}$ **2.** $z = \frac{0.5y}{x}$ **3.** direct variation; $y = -2x$

4. inverse variation; $y = \frac{1}{x}$ **5.** $y = \frac{2}{x - 1} - 1$

6. $y = \frac{2}{x - 5} + \frac{1}{2}$ **7.** vertical asymptote, $x = 3$; horizontal asymptote, $y = 1$ **8.** hole at $x = 8$; no vertical asymptote; horizontal asymptote, $y = 2$ **9.** hole at $x = -3$; vertical asymptote, $x = -2$; horizontal asymptote, $y = 0$ **10.** vertical asymptotes, $x = 2$ and $x = 3$; horizontal asymptote, $y = 0$ **11.** vertical asymptote, $x = -4$; horizontal asymptote, $y = -3$ **12.** vertical asymptote, $x = 1$; horizontal asymptote, $y = -2$

Chapter 9 Answers (continued)

13.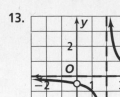

14.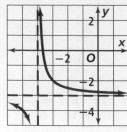

20. $\dfrac{2x^3 - x^2 + 9}{x^2(x^2 - 9)}$ **21.** $-\dfrac{4x - 49}{(x + 6)(x - 6)(x - 1)}$

22. $\dfrac{y^2 + 4y + 15}{3(y - 4)(y + 4)}$ **23.** Answers may vary.

Sample: Rational functions that have a common factor in the numerator and denominator have a removable discontinuity.

24. 1 **25.** $\dfrac{2xy - y}{3xy + x}$ **26.** 1 **27.** $-2, 6$ **28.** $-\dfrac{4}{11}$

29. 0 **30.** $-3, 1$ **31.** 4

32. Answers may vary. Sample: $\dfrac{3}{2x} + \dfrac{4}{3x} = \dfrac{17}{12}, x = 2$

33. $\dfrac{12}{7}$ h ≈ 1.71 h **34.** not mutually exclusive; $\dfrac{3}{4}$

35. mutually exclusive; 1 **36.** mutually exclusive; $\dfrac{3}{4}$ **37.** $\dfrac{1}{36}$

15. $\dfrac{3(x - 2)}{(x - 3)}; x \neq 3 \text{ or } -2$ **16.** $\dfrac{4}{x}; x \neq \dfrac{1}{2} \text{ or } 0$

17. $5(x - 4)(x + 4)$ **18.** $14(x - 2)(x + 5)^2$

19. $\dfrac{x^2 + 7x - 10}{(x + 5)(x - 5)}$ **20.** $\dfrac{3x^3 - x^2 + 4}{x^2(x^2 - 4)}$

21. $\dfrac{x^2(x + 3)}{(x - 1)(x + 2)}$ **22.** $\dfrac{y^2 + y + 21}{7(y - 1)(y + 1)}$

23. Answers may vary. Sample: A rational expression is in simplest form when its numerator and denominator have no common divisors. **24.** 4 **25.** $\dfrac{xy + y}{5xy - x}$ **26.** 12 **27.** 13

28. 2 **29.** 0 **30.** 2, 4 **31.** 2 **32.** Answers may vary.

Sample: $\dfrac{3}{4 + x} = \dfrac{x}{4}; -6, 2$ **33.** 1.2 h **34.** not mutually

exclusive; $\dfrac{5}{6}$ **35.** mutually exclusive; 1

36. mutually exclusive; $\dfrac{2}{3}$ **37.** $\dfrac{9}{169}$

Chapter Test, Form B

1. $y = -\dfrac{8}{x}$ **2.** $z = \dfrac{0.25x}{y}$ **3.** direct variation; $y = 4x$

4. inverse variation; $y = -\dfrac{2}{x}$ **5.** $y = \dfrac{4}{x + 2} - 1$

6. $y = \dfrac{4}{x - \frac{1}{3}} + 2$ **7.** vertical asymptote, $x = -4$;

horizontal asymptote, $y = 2$ **8.** hole at $x = 7$; no vertical asymptote; horizontal asymptote, $y = 6$ **9.** hole at $x = 4$; vertical asymptote, $x = -9$; horizontal asymptote, $y = 0$

10. vertical asymptotes, $x = 4$ and $x = -4$; horizontal asymptote, $y = 0$ **11.** vertical asymptote, $x = -2$; horizontal asymptote, $y = 3$ **12.** vertical asymptote, $x = 5$; horizontal asymptote, $y = -1$

13.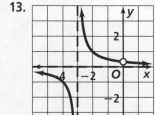

14.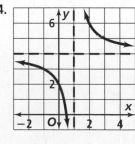

15. $-\dfrac{x}{2}; x \neq 7$ **16.** $\dfrac{8}{3}; x \neq 7 \text{ or } 5$ **17.** $3(x - 5)(x + 5)$

18. $8(x + 6)^2(x - 3)$ **19.** $\dfrac{x^2 + 7x - 12}{(x + 4)(x - 4)}$

Alternative Assessment, Form C

TASK 1 Scoring Guide:
Check students' work.

3 Student writes a correct function of inverse variation and correctly identifies the constant of variation. The independent and dependent variables, the domain and range, and the values of the asymptotes are all correct. The graph of the function is accurate and neatly drawn.

2 Student writes a correct function of inverse variation and correctly identifies the constant of variation. Student finds the domain, range, asymptotes, and dependent and independent variables with only minor errors. The graph of the function contains only minor errors.

1 Student writes a rational function that is not an inverse variation. There are major errors in determining the domain, range, and asymptotes of the function. Graph is not accurate.

0 Student makes no attempt, or no response is given.

TASK 2 Scoring Guide:
Check students' work.

3 Student correctly uses the function of inverse variation to find the value of the independent variable when the dependent variable is 3. Student accurately finds the value of the dependent variable when the independent variable is 6. Student correctly describes the end behavior of the function.

2 Student uses the function of inverse variation to find the value of the independent variable when the dependent variable is 3 with minor errors. Student finds the value of the dependent variable when the independent variable is 6 with minor errors. Student correctly describes the end behavior of the function.

1 Student does not correctly use the function to find the value of the independent variable when the dependent variable is 3. Student does not correctly find the value of the dependent variable when the independent variable is 6. Student describes the end behavior of the function incorrectly.

0 Student makes no attempt, or no response is given.

TASK 3 Scoring Guide:

a. time along first part of trip: $\frac{10}{r}$; time along second part of trip: $\frac{20}{r + 5}$; $t_{Total}(r) = \frac{30r + 50}{r(r + 5)}$, where r is the initial rate, $r \neq 0$, and $r \neq -5$.

b. domain: $\{r \mid r > 0\}$; range: $\{t \mid t > 0\}$; $t(r)$ has vertical asymptote at $r = 0$ and at $r = -5$. However, both of these r-values are not in the reasonable domain of the function. The horizontal asymptote is $t = 0$.

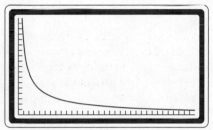

c. 37 mi/h

d. between 1 h, 18 min and 2 h, 20 min

3 Student correctly writes each rational expression or equation. Student determines correct domain, range, and asymptotes. Student solves the rational equation and inequality algebraically and graphically.

2 Student writes each rational expression or equation with only minor errors. Student finds the correct domain, range, and asymptotes with only minor errors. Student correctly solves one of the rational equations or inequalities algebraically or graphically.

1 Student writes correct rational expressions but adds incorrectly to get incorrect equation. Student correctly solves one of the rational equations or inequalities algebraically or graphically.

0 Student makes no attempt, or no response is given.

TASK 4 Scoring Guide:

a. 50%; 33%; 33%; 33%

b. 17%; independent

c. 67%; mutually exclusive

3 Student determines all probabilities correctly. Student shows the multiplication step in part b, and the addition step in part c. Student classifies b as independent and c as mutually exclusive.

2 Student determines all probabilities correctly. Student shows work in at least one of the parts b and c. Student correctly classifies at least one of events b and c.

1 Student determines some probabilities correctly. Student does not show all work, and does not correctly classify either events b or c.

0 Student makes no attempt, or no response is given.

Cumulative Review

1. D **2.** B **3.** A **4.** A **5.** C **6.** C **7.** B **8.** A **9.** D **10.** D
11. C **12.** B **13.** B **14.** C **15.** $\frac{15}{56}$ **16.** $\frac{3}{28}$ **17.** $y = 3x$
18. Answers may vary. Sample: You roll an even number with a number cube or you roll an odd number with a number cube. **19.** Check students' work.